A POLICY FOR
BRITISH AGRICULTURE

A POLICY FOR
BRITISH AGRICULTURE

by The Rt. Honble.
Lord Addison of Stallingborough
Minister of Agriculture 1930–1931

LONDON
VICTOR GOLLANCZ LTD
1939

To

the Memory of Those on the farm I
knew so well as a boy, and who
inspired my Love for the land

PRINTED IN GREAT BRITAIN BY PURNELL AND SONS, LTD. (T.U.)
PAULTON (SOMERSET) AND LONDON

PREFACE

A<small>T THE GENERAL ELECTION</small> of January 1910 we went round singing "God gave the Land for the People"! We called ourselves Radicals in those days, and I am not sure that we had not more of the real democratic stuff in us than some who call themselves Socialists these days.

Anyhow we meant it; because we thought it was the right thing that the ownership of Land should be a National responsibility in order that the best use could be made of it.

Nevertheless, National Ownership is only a means to an end. Unless we can build upon it a system that will lead to a better and a fuller use of our splendid land, that will turn back the tide of emigration from it and give a happier and more secure life to those who live and work upon it, we are not justified in the enterprise.

For my part, the faith I had in 1910 has never been dimmed, but has become fortified by the experiences of the years since then.

Destructive criticism is easy, but seldom of much use. The reader, therefore, will not find that I indulge in what is commonly described as "brick throwing". The descriptions of the present unsatisfactory state of affairs that are given in this book are given in order that they may help us to understand the reasons for it, to furnish guidance as to what we ought to do about it, how we ought to do it, and why.

For years past it has been an ambition of mine to write a book on this subject, but not being a ready writer it has been put aside. The invitation of Mr. Gollancz and the Members of the Left Book Club has, however, impelled me to do the best I can.

My thanks are due to many friends in the public service who have supplied me with figures and other data; to

Mr. Sidney Foster of the Milk Marketing Board for the figures relating to Milk and Milk Products; to Mr. H. B. Pointing, Editor of the *Land Worker*, for much valuable material, and to Mr. Ernest Davies for his Memorandum on Compensation that appears as Appendix III.

In particular I am grateful to my wife for her constant help in the preparation and writing of this book.

ADDISON.

Peterley Farm,
Gt. Missenden,
Bucks.
April 19*th*, 1938.

CONTENTS

Chapter 1

Preliminary Considerations

Agriculture, many Industries—Our National Advantages—Surprising Decline in Spite of Them—Exodus from the Countryside—The Case of Those who would Disregard Agriculture—The Case for Cheapness—Wages and the Prices of Products—The Justness of Good Wages—We should Refuse to Accept Poverty—Need for a Good Standard of Living for Home Producers—Fundamental Alterations of Present System Required—War Dangers—A Fuller Life should be our Aim.

AGRICULTURE IS NOT one industry. It is many. The selection, breeding and rearing of cattle, the art of the shepherd as his eye takes in at a glance the ailing ones amongst his sheep scattered over the hillside, the complicated processes of mixed arable farming, the work of the fruit-grower as he selects his stock for grafting and prunes and sprays and cares for his trees, the work of the poultry farmer, of the glass-house cultivator and of many more are widely different from one another in the problems they present and in the knowledge and experience they demand. They are indeed as different from one another as are many other distinctive industries. But they have this in common; they depend in one way or another on the use of Mother Earth.

The case begins, then, with the Land. But the Land requires that there should be people apt and understanding in its use. The use of it depends also upon the demand for its products.

We therefore have to consider the Land, the Producer and the Product. These three go together. If they are properly associated success will result. If not, failure.

This book is concerned with these matters as they affect us in our homeland of Great Britain and with the problems and policies that arise out of them.

Our natural advantages are so great that the present distresses of Agriculture must indicate serious follies or misfits in the system we live under. Look at some of the advantages.

In proportion to the whole extent of this Island there is an unusually large area of land that might be made productive. Much of it has been allowed to become neglected for reasons which we shall set forth, but its possibilities have been established and they are still with us. Nevertheless for centuries past much of it has been well cultivated and our produce is famous for its high quality. People come from all parts of the world to buy our Breeding Stocks because of their excellence. The yield per acre of corn is higher than that of most other lands, and many of our home-grown fruits and vegetables are unsurpassed and rarely equalled. There is still no better apple than our Cox's Orange Pippin.

These things betoken not only suitable Land, but that there is amongst our farmers and agricultural labourers a great wealth of skill and of practical ability.

There is, moreover, within a short distance of every farm in the country, the best food market in the world. Apart, also, from this market, which every day is taking in supplies from the ends of the earth, it is proved that there is amongst our own population a great multitude that is not getting enough food and particularly of the kinds of food that we are exceptionally well able to produce.

Finally, where in all the world shall we find a place so pleasant and so restful as this British countryside?

How surprising it is, then, to find that in spite of these favourable conditions, millions of acres of land have passed out of active cultivation and that the process is continuing; that an increasing extent of good land is reverting to tufts of inferior grass, to brambles and weeds, and often to the reedy growth that betrays water-logging; that multitudes of farms are beset with dilapidated buildings, and that a great and rapid diminution is taking place in the number of those who find employment upon them.

These declines have shown themselves in varying degrees for the last fifty years, but during recent years they have been accelerated in a surprising manner. A silent but dramatic exodus is in process. The number of those employed on the land (whole-time and part-time) has been declining all these years, but it has diminished by more than 100,000 since 1930. The total in Great Britain has fallen by nearly 300,000 since 1891.[1] Since the beginning of the present century nearly a quarter of a million workers have quietly drifted from the country to the town, and this whilst for many of these self-same years the chances of employment in the towns were worse than we have any previous record of. I do not know how many Israelites there were in the flight from Egypt, but we must indeed look far to find a shifting of the population to compare with this.

The causes will not be difficult to discover as we come to a closer examination of the case, but it is a national loss of a peculiarly vital kind that a great body of people skilled in the production of food so much required and with a type of skill that can only be slowly and laboriously acquired, should be dissipated like this, and that the children of these cultivators, as they grow up, should turn away from their home surroundings and the places they surely love. It is, and can only be, because they feel that the life and opportunities open to them in their native village are not good enough.

There are, however, some people who do not seem to regard this decay of Agriculture with much dismay. They are so obsessed by the worship of cheapness at any cost that they overlook its obvious concomitants in keeping down the standard of wages and purchasing power, and the spread of desolation over their own countryside. Their eyes seem to be fixed only on overseas trade, forgetting that, even as it is, the purchasing power derived from the sale of home-produced food enables the farming

[1] For detailed figures see Appendix I.

community to spend £80 with our town industries for every £100 spent by the whole of our overseas Empire.

Before we have finished with this book we shall see that nothing but good would follow from the perfectly attainable result of increasing our home food production by at least half as much again, but, regarded only as an undeveloped market for our industrial products, a restored countryside is of first-rate importance.

There are other important reasons why such a restoration should be aimed at, but before we come to them, let us look a little closer at the two sets of considerations which lie behind the neglect of this great industry. They are not usually stated in the raw, of course; but, in fact, they involve, first, a sort of rationalisation of shipping tonnage and, second, the exaltation of cheapness.

The first case, in short, is this: We can import beef from the Argentine cheaper than we can grow it here under conditions that will give a decent and secure living to home producers, so why grow cattle? And the same argument is, or may be, applied to many other major food commodities. The case is supported by pointing out that meat production requires the importation of feeding-stuffs which, in themselves, are more bulky than the meat they lead to. Not long ago[1] an article by Mr. Colin Clark in the *Spectator* summed up the philosophy of this School of Economists very forcibly. It leads, indeed, as he pointed out, to the question as to whether Agriculture is a "liability" or an "asset"—even to the enquiry as to whether "the best policy is to close down British Agriculture completely and to import all our food requirements from overseas".

It is of course true that a box of eggs weighs less than the food the hen consumes to produce them; a side of bacon weighs less than the food the pig would eat. But where does this kind of argument lead us? We can put aside the pursuit of any insensate policy of national self-sufficiency, but in this mad world we cannot disregard the

[1] *Spectator*, August 23rd, 1937.

dangers of war. However, leaving that aside for the moment, the argument that it would save tonnage if we cut out the importation of feeding-stuffs and concentrated on the finished product cannot be confined to food products. It would apply with equal force to lots of other things. A ready-made door, for example, weighs less than the timber out of which it was made, so does a pair of boots as compared with the hides that provided the leather; imported iron-ore weighs more than the steel it gives rise to; a bale of cotton more than a shirt, and so on.

What, also, are the people going to do who would be put out of work by this policy? If the men, women and children (say, four millions in all) dependent directly upon the cultivation of the land are to be sacrificed on the altar of tonnage economy, where are they going to live? Presumably in the towns where in many cases there are already more people than can be found work for. Also if the tonnage argument is to guide our policy many of the workers in the town would find themselves in exactly the same position as the food producers.

Also how under this scheme are we going to pay for the finished goods that we should require to import in such vastly greater quantities, seeing that our manufactures are largely based on the importation of raw materials? It is economics in blinkers with a vengeance.

The only people who would be fortified by plans of this sort would be the birth-control enthusiasts. It is national *hari-kari*. Nothing less. There would, however, be a great increase in the number of hares, rabbits and other vermin and more occupation for poachers.

The worship of Cheapness is much more plausible.

Abundance of food by all means! But to what extent is cheapness of food to dominate our policy?

When a body of Trade Unionists approaches their employers and asks for an increase of wages they do not enquire what the result will be if they are successful in the cost of the article they help to produce. In any case they have not the accounting material at their disposal to enable them to do so, and, if they had, it might not affect the justice of their claim. It is true that precise accountancy has often shown that the share of labour in the ultimate cost of things is much less than is suggested when bargains over wages are being conducted, but in the majority of cases the claim for better wages is based on something that is fundamental. It is: that the workers are doing useful work and helping to produce something the people need and that they are entitled *in return for their labour* to such payment as will enable them and their families to have a decent standard of existence. A claim of this kind is entirely righteous. It ought to be admitted as a universal rule. Those who neither toil nor spin would be hard put to it to establish a case for their income on as just a basis as this.

As a matter of fact so long as it is confined to a general proposition there are few people who would disagree that it is right and proper that people who are rendering a service that the Community needs are entitled to a living that will provide them with a good home, plenty of food, respectable clothes and the other things in reason that are accepted as part of a civilised standard of life— *because they are rendering that service.*

It is when we try to apply this wholesome doctrine that the trouble begins. For the present, however, let us be clear that it is right, and that we ought to apply it if we can; that it should be applicable to all concerned in production whether of a ton of coals or a ton of potatoes or of any of the other numberless things that people want.

If this is right, it follows that, when a thing is wanted and a proper case for its production is made out, we are not entitled to aim at its being provided at a price that will mean the degradation of the life of those who produce it. We have no right to buy coals at the price of the malnutrition of the miner's child, or potatoes at that of the agricultural labourer's. When the case for cheapness is pressed to this extent it means the entrenchment and acceptance of poverty as a necessary evil, which it is not.

It means that coolie labour standards are justifiable. If we have not income enough to pay a just price then it is our standard of income that is wrong. We *ought* to have money enough.

The fact is, however, that the price people have to pay for things—particularly for their food—is often very much greater than the price the man receives who produces it. Sometimes two, or even three times as much. And where this increase of price is greater than it ought properly to be, serious harm is being done. Those who render any necessary service in transport, storage, marketing or distribution are just as entitled to be adequately paid as the producer is, but any needless increase in these costs must be wrong because, at the end, the coals are still the same coals, the potatoes the same potatoes, neither more nor less.

It is to be noted that this argument depends upon there being a "proper case" for the production of the commodity in question. Nobody would suggest that there would be such a case for, say, the British cultivation of bananas or of cocoanuts, but there is clearly such a case for many of the products of the home agriculture—milk, meat, eggs and poultry, corn (on some lands), many vegetables and some fruits, because of the established suitability of our land and climate and the renowned quality of these products. Prosperity and contentment amongst their producers must depend upon our being able somehow or other to secure for them the just rights of the decent livelihood to which they are entitled. This condition also is essential if we are to make progress in restoring good land to its proper use and in arresting the drain of hardy and experienced people from it.

But it will not happen of itself. It will only come about if we shape our measures to see that it does. It is also foolish to ignore the fact that, in their very essence, the measures required for this purpose must differ profoundly from the system we now live under, or that their introduction will be attended with many difficulties. At the present time the sale of the products of husbandry depends upon what is called "the market" obtaining its supplies from the producer for as little as it can induce him to part with them for, and, in the end, persuading the consumer to pay as much as possible for them. This latter—the consumer's price—as already said, is often much greater than it need be by the conglomeration of agencies of one kind or another which have come into existence between the sale by the producer and the counter at which the housewife buys her supplies.

The results are damaging at both ends. If the producer has to accept a price which cripples his enterprise and keeps down the standard of life and wages on the land it is destroying the basis of progress. If the housewife, at the other end, has to pay more than a rational and well-conducted system would require, then she has to buy less than she ought and risk her children being ill-nourished. This, in its turn, is damaging to the whole community. But it happens every day under the present system. It cannot but happen. Altogether it is a wicked system.

There is no doubt that plenty of food can be produced. *Our aim, therefore, should be twofold.* To supply the people with the plenty they need, and, at the same time, enable the home-producer to make his contribution towards the provision of that plenty under self-respecting and encouraging conditions.

It seems simple to state our objective like that, but there are dense thickets of interest and of habit in the way. But let us keep this objective clearly in mind.

It must be true also that, with this fertile land available, with this great body of skill and experience amongst farmers and workers, with this demand so close to their homesteads for the products of their labours which they are so fitted to produce, we are possessed of priceless national assets which it would be a crime to waste.

In a later chapter I shall try to indicate the adjustments that might be made in the Plan of Development that is recommended for diminishing the peril to which this country might be exposed in time of war. It is no good pretending that we may not be exposed to such a peril. We may. The present dreadful drift of affairs makes it quite a possibility that such a madness may overtake us. If it did, it would provide dramatic evidence of the wisdom of restoring agriculture. We can never be self-supporting perhaps; but it will be easy to prove that we can and ought, apart from any such dreadful event, make a much better use of our land than we do. And, remember, we cannot produce skilled workers quickly or accelerate the processes of nature in the growth of food.

There is another, and a greater reason even than any mentioned so far, why we should not waste our precious heritage in land. Agriculture is more than a group of industries. It is a life. A life for men and women and children. And where in all the world shall we find a place in which life might be so pleasant and so full as in this British countryside? It behoves us, with all the wisdom and courage we can command, to make a better use of our advantages so that a fuller and a happier life may be enjoyed by more of our fellow-citizens. This is the great and final purpose of it all. For my part, as one who passed his boyhood amongst the fields and lanes of England and who has never failed to be drawn towards them, I can think of no life pleasanter than that which might be found amongst them. The same is true with others of the valleys of Wales and of the lowlands and glens of Scotland.

> "'Tis life whereof our nerves are scant,
> More life and fuller that we want."

PART I

PRESENT CONDITIONS

PART I

SECTION I

Chapter II

The People Concerned—The Disposition of the Countryman—*The Landowner*—The Decline of the Partnership of the Owner who Lets his Land—Limitation of the Power of the Landlord by the Agricultural Holdings Acts—*The Owner-Occupier*—His Present Poverty.

THE RIGHT METHOD of approach to the subject before us is to take account, in the first place, of things as they are. Therefore this and some succeeding chapters will be devoted to that purpose. The People immediately affected, the present condition of the Land itself, and the methods of the disposal of its Produce, are the subjects concerned.

The persons directly affected are the Landlord, the Farmer and the Labourer. But one preliminary comment upon the general character of those who work on the land is called for, because it must not be forgotten that, whatever system may be adopted, these are the people whose co-operation must be obtained.

The Countryman, as a rule, is lonely. It is so with the farmer as he goes about his fields turning over in his mind the many things that form the daily nature of his calling—the outlook of the weather, the condition of the crops, the management of his stock and many more. It is even more so with the labourer, as he slowly works his way across the field with his hoe or on some other task. He can commune with no one but himself for hour after hour. Sometimes to outward seeming they are slow and dull, and perhaps they often are, but it is much more a cautiousness that arises out of the nature of their occupation. They have many amongst them who are nature's gentlemen; the salt of the earth they till.

The countryman, as a result, is intensely individualistic. He is exceedingly difficult to compel, but he is surprisingly adaptable. At the present time he is adapting himself with remarkable rapidity to changes in methods of cultivation, of the management of live-stock and of the preparation of his produce for the market that are almost revolutionary as compared with those that prevailed even as lately as just before the war.

More than once in history attempts have been made, with disastrous results, to force a system upon the land which failed to take account sufficiently of the disposition, as well as the interests, of the countryman who was responsible for the work. It was so in this country at the time of the great enclosures; and the price was terrible. Indeed we are paying it still. It has been so, lately, in some districts of Russia. It does not mean that the purpose of the change is necessarily wrong, but it does mean that it has encountered needless and perhaps fatal difficulties, because those in charge did not bear well enough in mind that what we *want* to do must be conditioned by what we *can* do. This is not timidity. It is sense.

During recent years there has been a great increase in the amount of land that is in public ownership, but more than 90 per cent of the Land is still in private ownership.

The Landowner

The Landowner, except where he himself is the occupier, has practically ceased to be a partner in husbandry. It is a rare thing nowadays to find farms where the landowner has provided new farm buildings or brought the old ones up to date; where he helps the farmer with the cost of fencing or field drainage, or with improving the fertility of the land. The old estates also have been extensively broken up and the active partnership that used to attach to them has disappeared.

I am not concerned to discuss the morality of the private ownership of land. Human nature being what it is I suppose that, if it had been physically possible, we should have had private claims pegged out in the air and on the sea. Indeed the claims for foreshore rights that still exist are proof that it would have been so, and it was my duty as late as 1930, as Minister of Agriculture, to acquire for the State (happily for a small sum) certain foreshore reclamation rights that still existed along the shores of the Lincolnshire Wash under a Charter dating from Tudor times.

There is a fiction, of course, that the land belongs to the King as Head of the State. But private ownership and control of the land has been in practical operation for centuries, and we must take it as it is. Like other systems it has its vices and its redeeming features. The depopulation of whole districts in Scotland for the purpose of Sport was a crime that remains unqualified. The extensive expropriations of land that accompanied the Enclosure Acts of the late eighteenth and early nineteenth centuries in England destroyed a splendid and independent peasantry, but they did lead in many places to improved drainage, to better equipment and to better cultivation of the land. The wealth that followed from these enclosures and that accrued during the French wars gave the Landowner and the Squire a power and dominance in country districts greater perhaps than ever before.

The system which then became predominant was different from, and far less human than, the semi-feudal system it displaced, which had given a share of responsibility as well as of independence to all the village community. The enclosures enriched the landowners and the large farmers and created a great social gulf between them and the peasantry who had been deprived of all their former rights and who were forced down to a wretched serfdom dependent upon a monetary pittance supplemented by relief in kind that kept them chained to their poverty.

That gulf has not yet been bridged. The memory of that time has sunk deep into the mind and outlook of the labourer and is still a tremendous obstacle to his enterprise and progress.

The Landowners and the Country Squires of that time, however, did develop a practice of equipping their estates with farm buildings and with such cottages as they thought good enough for the labourer. They helped their tenants with drainage, fencing and with many forms of land improvement and maintenance. There was amongst them, no doubt, a proportion of the dissolute and the extravagant, but it is true to say that, generally, land equipment was regarded as a landowner's duty and the tradition was to take a pride in assisting in the maintenance of a good standard of husbandry.

The last quarter of the nineteenth century witnessed a rapid decline and during the present century the pace has quickened. Successive depressions in agriculture, the burdening of estates with annuitants, death duties and higher taxation led to large-scale sales whenever land happened to become dear, and, collectively, have led to the disappearance of the old practices and to widespread deterioration of land equipment. It is true that here and there, where the landowner's family happens to possess town estates, collieries, or some other source of income other than agriculture, the farms are kept up, but these cases are few and far between and exist for the most part as reminders of days that are gone. From one end of the country to the other the old mansions are being left, taken for schools, or for country hotels, acquired by County Councils and other Bodies for different purposes. The industrial magnate and the new rich have taken some of these places, often for sport and sometimes for display, but their interests are not with the land and consequently we see their estates being disposed of by the next generation. Changes of social habit, the development of city life and interests, travel and many other altered customs have played their part. The results of all these changes today is that the neglected condition of millions of acres of good land calls aloud for wise capital expenditure.

The regret of the landowning class at the disappearance of their former share in supporting land maintenance and improvement was sincerely and dramatically stated in the House of Lords on July 20th, 1937, by Lord Hastings. He was speaking on the second Reading of the Agriculture Bill and, commenting upon the fact that the State was obliged to come in and make contributions towards the liming and artificial manuring of Land. Lord Hastings said[1]:—

"What a ghastly confession it is to those who were brought up in the strict tradition of land ownership which prevailed universally not more than thirty years ago! It is positively shocking to think of the need that a Bill should be introduced into Parliament including a land fertility clause. In those days it was the proudest and first duty of every landowner to make himself responsible for that fertility. In those days he had the power to enforce it, and in the main he had the means to make his own essential contribution to it. Today he has neither the power nor the means."

Lord Hastings went on to attribute the blame for this state of affairs to mistaken State Policy including, no doubt, the far-reaching effect of Death Duties. As to that, however, he entered into no particulars but his statement that the landowner today has neither the power nor the means to play his part in the maintenance of agriculture is undeniably true.

There are other circumstances which should be noticed in connection with the decline in the partnership of the landlord. For some time before the war the costs of Estate Management had been rising and it is estimated that on well-managed estates they took £30 out of every £100 received in rents, and such costs must have risen considerably since the war. This increase in the cost of estate management, together with reductions in rent which had to be conceded during the agricultural depression, meant that the returns landlords were receiving from their agricultural land represented a smaller and smaller percentage of its presumed capital value and increased the disposition to

[1] *Hansard*, July 20th, 1937, Col. 699.

sell whenever a favourable moment should occur. Nowadays we find that those whose interests formerly would
have been in the management of their estates are more
and more on the Directorates of great business concerns
and their main interests are diverted from the land
accordingly.

Apart from this the different Agricultural Holdings Acts,
(so significant of the different regard that the State has
for land as distinguished from other property) have progressively diminished the landlord's power and turned
him more and more into a mere rent receiver. There were
various Acts before 1906, but the Act of that year, afterwards consolidated in the Agricultural Holdings Act of
1908, made two important inroads into the power of the
landlord. It took away the restrictions which had previously
been common in farm agreements upon the freedom of
the tenant in regard to cropping and, more important still,
limited the freedom of the landlord to repossess himself
of his property. Unless he could show good cause he was
forthwith required to compensate the tenant for the loss
or expense he might be put to because of his having to
quit his holding. This last provision was put into a still
more definite form in the Agriculture Act of 1920 by
defining the amount of compensation that the farmer
should receive for disturbance. As Orwin and Peel say:[1] "It
is now almost impossible to remove a tenant for any
reason except bad farming."

The Act of 1920 went further in another respect. It
gave the tenant a right to demand arbitration upon the
amount of his rent, and if the demand were refused by his
landlord and the tenant gave notice and quitted his holding
in consequence, he could obtain compensation as if the
notice to quit had been given by the landlord.

The motive behind these Agricultural Holdings Act
was that, since the landlord was becoming progressively
unable to play his part in the industry, the tenant should

[1] *The Tenure of Agricultural Land*, Orwin and Peel, Cambridge
University Press, 1926, 2nd ed., p. 3.

be safeguarded whenever he made efforts to improve the
land he farmed. Indeed the Acts provide in this way
a sort of Statutory recognition of the decline of the old
system.

The Landowners, to whom reference has been made
so far, own rather more than two-thirds of the land that
is described in the Agricultural Returns as "under cultivation" and practically all the rough grazing, hillside,
moorlands and other land. But there is another large class
of owners—known as Owner-occupiers—who farm their
own land. Their numbers increased from time to time
with the break-up of estates but they received a great
addition during the widespread land sales that took place
after the Great War, from 1919 onwards.

According to an estimate prepared for me at the Ministry
of Agriculture in 1930, the number of those who farm their
own land in England and Wales increased by 98,000
between 1919 and 1927, and the acreage of the land thus
farmed by the owner increased from over three to a little
over nine million acres. This means, therefore, that about
a third of the farm land of the country has passed over
to the farmers themselves. In the vast majority of cases
they have millstones of mortgages hung round their
necks.

At those times when land was making a good price,
the former owners, finding that the commodity they were
possessed of had gone up in value, decided that it was a
good time to sell. Nothing is to be gained by "throwing
bricks" at them on that account. In this they acted no
differently than the holder of any other commodity
might do who, under the present order of things, finds that
his possessions are making a good price and decides to
take advantage of a good market—whether he sells stocks
and shares, carpets, boots, or anything else.

In this case, however, the effects have been far-reaching
and disastrous. All over the country farmers bought their
farms because they wanted to retain their home and

occupation—but they bought at a high price. They usually had to borrow two-thirds of the purchase price on mortgage and, for the rest, often put in all the money they had. Not infrequently some of the balance came from bank overdrafts on the security of their stock or general credit. The rate of interest payable on these mortgages was usually 5 or $5\frac{1}{2}$ per cent.

There is abundant evidence to show that the farmers were well aware of the disadvantages they were incurring in putting what money they had into the purchase of their farms. The evidence given before the Havisham Committee in 1912 and that has accumulated since shows well enough that a great majority of them would have preferred to remain as tenants and use their capital for farming purposes. It was security of tenure that they wanted and the sacrifices they made were made in order to obtain it.

As the post-war boom passed, prices fell—both of agricultural produce and of land—and ten years after the war there were extensive land sales, particularly in the eastern counties, where land was sold for no more than the mortgage. In several cases indeed the sales could not be effected at all because there were no bidders at prices that could be accepted. It is probably an understatement to say that 90 per cent of the owner-occupiers who bought their farms during the boom period of 1919–21 have lost every penny they contributed to the purchase, and that much of the land is not now worth the mortgage which was obtained upon it.

The result is that in a large number of cases the owner-occupiers are worse off for working capital than the average tenant farmer. Their money has disappeared in land depreciation, and they have to carry on as best they can on such overdrafts as the banks will allow or by being continually in debt for feeding-stuffs and other requirements. For similar reasons also the practice of paying by instalments for live-stock has increased enormously so that thousands of farmers are not really the owners of the cattle that may be seen on their own pastures.

There are, of course, in different parts of the country many small owner-occupiers whose families have worked their own land for generations and who are fairly well off, but the aggregate amount of land so farmed is a very small portion of the whole. During the slump in land prices that occurred round about 1930 a number of enterprising farmers bought land cheap and are now in a good position; but when generous allowance has been made for these exceptions the account here given of the position of the owner-occupiers is abundantly true of the vast majority.

To expect these men to improve or repair their buildings, to provide water supplies, to drain their land, or to keep their fences in good order is to expect the impossible. Everywhere you find their buildings in a deplorable state, roofs defective, doors broken down and the walls often affording but little shelter. The farm roads are neglected and the farm yards in wet weather are deep in slush and liquid manure; the gates are broken down, or patched up anyhow, and the fields often enough, with their vistas of weeds and rubbish, cry aloud for land drainage.

They have no money wherewith to put the place in order.

PART I

SECTION II

Chapter III

The Farmer and Farming

The Farmer—Preservation of the Landscape—Special Features of Farming—The Labour-employing Farmer—New Methods—Young Farmers—Need for Training and Good Openings—The Family Farmers—The Farmer's Toleration of Existing Marketing Methods— His Helplessness.

THE FOX-HUNTING FARMERS of the old days have gone. The last of them disappeared in the depression of the 1880's. They were good material for the picturesque writer and the artist, but there were never so many of them, in proportion to the rest, as was popularly supposed. They were the descendants, both by race and by tradition, of the wealthy farmers who multiplied after the great enclosures. It was still a crime to shoot a fox when I was a boy in North Lincolnshire although the body of more than one ravager of hen-roosts could have been found in the turnips with a charge of shot inside him.

Farmers are as diverse as the many industries they represent; but they have some things in common that we ought to take account of.

The fact, already noticed, that they work in isolation is the biggest obstacle of all to their co-operation either in buying, selling, or in other ways. It makes them inclined also to be suspicious—especially of a denizen of Whitehall. But, like most other people who live in daily contact with Nature, they respond to frankness even if it is a statement that is not altogether to their liking. I think that the grumbling habit with which, as a class, they are usually credited, is due, partly, to their daily struggle with forces they cannot control, but, still more, to an unfortunate practice of their spokesmen. I used to think sometimes when it was my lot to receive deputations from the National Farmers' Union that if they would spend as much time in working out practical proposals for benefiting their industry as they did in building up a body of complaints, they would have deserved better of their members. I suppose, again, it was mainly due to the isolation of their ordinary life; it made it difficult even for leaders to develop the frame of mind that enables men to think in common, as so many industrialists have to do.

Let us look, however, at the credit as well as the debit side, for our business is to try and understand so that we may the better appreciate what ought to be done, and how to do it.

There is one fact that never comes into agricultural talks, but which we ought not to forget. The British landscape we love so much has been preserved by farming. The pasture-lands, the fields and hedges bespeak generations of loving care. Later on we shall have to deplore and account for the neglect that has spread so widely, but the very neglect itself should help us to realise what things would be like if it were not for farming—thistles, nettles, and weeds and all manner of rubbish spreading over good land, offending the eye and telling the story of a struggle that has been abandoned.

Partly because he is "a sticker" like Britishers generally, partly because of the nature of his occupation and, more still, because he loves the land and will not let it go, the farmer has stuck to his tillage even when he was grousing and when times were bad.

The raw material of the industrialist manufacturer is used up, but it is not so with agriculture. Given good husbandry the soil not only remains, but its fertility is maintained year after year, generation after generation. How different in this respect is the practice that has been followed in our home land from that which has turned great tracts of the United States and some parts of Canada into deserts. If anyone wants an object lesson of the disastrous results of the prodigal using up of the treasures of nature in a rush to get rich quick, instead of the frugal use and careful preservation of the riches of the soil, he should read the record of the waste of natural resources which is now causing so much anxiety in the United States.[1] Reckless destruction of moisture-holding trees and the tearing up of soil-holding turf have meant that drought and dust-storms have had free play and have swept the soil away to the distant ocean leaving bare stones where once was a wide and fertile district. The amount of desert in the United States has increased for these reasons by no less than fifty million acres during the past twenty years (or nearly twice the cultivated and grass area of England and Wales together), and we are told that a further hundred million acres are doomed. There is full justification for the story of the old Nebraska farmer who was sitting in his porch during a dust-storm and was asked what he was watching. He replied: "I am counting the Kansas farms as they go by." British farming has preserved our superb countryside. Let us not forget this when we are impatient with the farmer and deplore his grumbling.

There are some other special features of farm work that ought to be borne in mind and which distinguish it from general industry. Except here and there farming is dependent on outside assistance for the provision of its capital equipment, buildings, cottages, drainage, fences and the rest—and you cannot make the best use of land unless these essential things are there. Next, the farmer is dependent on the weather, and therefore can only plan his productions with the knowledge that nature may step in and ruin his best efforts. Further he cannot shut down or curtail his production when things are not going well as a manufacturer can. He must still go on, because next year, or even the year after, may be jeopardised if he does not. Alongside this also he must wait a long time for any return on his expenditure. Some things can be speeded up it is true, but it must take three years or so to produce a milk cow. He cannot accelerate the growth of wool on a sheep of or a crop of wheat. Next, if things are doing badly he cannot quickly, and sometimes not at

[1] *Rich Land, Poor Land*, by Stuart Chase, McGraw-Hill Book Co., Inc.

all, turn from one kind of production to another. The change-over, say, from stock-raising to dairying, although both are concerned with cattle, takes a considerable time; it requires a different type of stock, as well as different buildings and accommodation in many cases. Very important also is the difference between him and the industrialist in that he cannot work to order on a schedule of prices either for what he buys or for what he sells. This vital difference will have much to do with the theme of this book, but it should be noted in passing.

There is no necessity, save as it affects our general purpose, to describe the different types of farmers, but we must distinguish the small and large farmers employing labour who are chiefly engaged in mixed farming, (although with a rapidly increasing degree of specialisation) from the family-farmer, including the smallholder, who depends almost entirely on his own work and on that of his family.

It is the former class, especially in arable districts— whether they have farmed under a landlord or become occupier-owners—that has been hit so badly by the periodic slumps which we accept as if they were some inescapable dispensation of Providence instead of being the results of our follies, and which, under a rational and properly controlled system we could prevent.

The larger, labour-employing, farmers of this class have been the chief inheritors of the bad traditions of the post-enclosure days which gave us the Tolpuddle Martyrs. They have a heavy responsibility for the niggardly outlook upon the interests of their real partner, the labourer, which has had such disastrous results. Happily this outlook is altering rapidly, not only because of the growing shortage of skilled and dependable labour, but because the type and outlook of the farmers themselves are changing very much.

In agriculture, as in other industries, there are many bold, and often successful, innovations; and it is probably true to say that, despite the decline that marks the industry as a whole, there are many more farmers than there were who are ready to adopt new methods so far as they can.

In the main, I think, this is attributable to three things; the spread of mechanical contrivances dependent upon the use of the petrol engine and electricity; the influence of the younger men who have taken courses of instruction at agricultural institutes or colleges, and the work of the Agricultural Organisers and Experts employed by the County Councils and the Ministry of Agriculture. It will be worth while to glance at these three because the future will certainly make increased demands on all of them.

Despite their intense, and often obstinate, conservatism and dislike of change, farmers do in fact display a remarkable adaptability. It has been said: "Capitalism will do nothing to adapt the work to the man. It asks the man to fit the job and discards him if he fails to do it."[1] So far as this is applicable to agriculture, it can be claimed that both the farmer and the labourer have stood the test well. A Combine Harvester is really a complicated set of machinery, but somehow or other the farms have produced men who can manage it and keep it running. It is common enough nowadays to find agricultural workers managing electric milking apparatus, sterilisers and suchlike and taking a lively interest in the results of bacterial counts. In each case the farmer has been responsible for the introduction of these things and for directing their use.

In a recent delightful book on "Farming England"[2] Mr. A. G. Street said: "I have found it much easier to teach a good ploughman to drive a tractor than to teach a good engineer the art and mystery of ploughing. The one is a factory job which can be learnt fairly quickly; the other requires a lifetime of labour and love, and, at the end, one is still learning."

In times past it has happened more than once that a man has conducted successfully new methods of cropping or cultivation, and yet not been imitated by his neighbours. It is puzzling to find out why not. This was the case with Mr. Prout and his son in continuous corn growing

[1] *New Statesman and Nation*, July 31st, 1937.
[2] *Farming England*, by A. G. Street, Messrs. Batsford, p. 14.

at Sawbridgworth in Herts for more than thirty years from 1870 onwards. Mr. Baylis, in another farm, struck out a new line in Berkshire from 1875 and was so successful that, up to 1917, he had extended his enterprises to more than 12,000 acres. Mr. F. P. Chamberlain is still successfully adopting similar methods at Crowmarsh Battle Farm in Oxfordshire, and other cases could be quoted.[1]

The chief reasons why these examples were not widely imitated appear to be these: the depressions of the last quarter of the nineteenth century had sunk deep into the minds of farmers; their innate conservatism and reluctance to change were very powerful, but the bitter experiences they had had made them fearful of incurring new risks. Most of all—and this applies particularly to the large class of owner-occupiers who had to buy their farms in the post-war land boom—the farmers had no money to finance new operations and the inability of the landlord to play his part, where they were tenants, left them struggling on as best they could in the old ways.

Nevertheless, during recent years there have been many advances in Specialisation, but before taking note of them reference should be made to the younger farmers and to the response to the work of the County Organisers and other experts. Amongst the younger farmers, and especially amongst those who have had the advantage of work at the Agricultural Colleges and Institutes, there is a body of men who, if they were given a decent chance, would make a full use of modern knowledge and practice, both in cultivation and in the preparation of their produce for the market. At the present time most of them are not within shouting distance of a chance of any sort because the existing system shuts out all men without capital.

At this place let me dispose once and for all of the silly idea that some people entertain that farming is a job anybody can take up. It has to be learnt like any

[1] Details of these cases are given by C. S. Orwin, *Farming without Livestock*, Clarendon Press, 1930, and *The Future of Farming*, Clarendon Press, 1930.

other craft, and the more specialised it becomes the greater is the need for instruction and training. It is true that some men, with ready aptitudes and the instincts of management, have left other occupations and taken up farming and done well; but without exception I think they will be found to be of the industrious, eager-to-learn, ready-witted type who would make good at almost anything. Thousands of good fellows after the war courted nothing but loss and disappointment because they had been impressed with this mistaken notion. In his book on "Farming England"[1] Mr. Street tells a story of some business man who had tried his hand at farming and lost a lot of money and who announced: "I shall go back to town business. I can make money there easily enough. Any fool can make money in town, but it needs a genius to do it out of farming." He was a lucky man if he could make money "easily", in the town but perhaps he was letting himself go in his chagrin. The moral of it, however, is plain enough. We must have a system that will encourage and make use of the fine body of experienced land workers we already have. Recruits will come right enough if we get the industry on to a right basis, but they will have to learn the job.

In nearly every county these days there are Specialists employed by the Councils, and partly paid for by the Ministry of Agriculture, whose work it is to help farmers by consultation and advice on cultivation problems, on livestock, on market gardening, poultry raising and other matters as well as to give short courses of instruction up and down their districts. At the beginning, these men's services were not fully appreciated, but for some years past now practically all of them have been "run off their legs" by the demands made on them. They are carefully chosen, well-trained men and the increasing appreciation of their work is the best evidence we can have of a more alert outlook on the part of many farmers.

There have always been Specialists, as the diverse character of the industry denotes, but the work of the

[1] Loc. cit., p. 51.

county staffs have helped to extend and improve specialisation in many directions. The cultivation of fruit,
vegetables, flowers, cheese-making, poultry rearing and
fattening, and many more, have specially belonged to
the family-farmer or the smallholder, but lately there have
been big extensions of these specialisations. Mr. Hosier
in Wiltshire has become famous not only by his large-
scale open-air dairying, but by the establishment on open
land of big units of production of poultry and pigs, each
with their special staff supported by a central organisation. In South Lincolnshire, where we now see vast expanses of flowers and vegetables, on what, not long ago,
was arable or mixed farming land, the large-scale production of bulbs, flowers, celery, potatoes, and other
market-garden produce has changed the face of the
district. Similarly, every year we get more cases of large-
scale, highly mechanised farming, and these do not
always mean the employment in the aggregate of less
labour. I shall refer later on to the particulars of a large
farm of more than 6,000 acres which represents the
amalgamation of a number of smaller farms, where many
of the fields have been thrown together and where the
latest machinery is used as much as possible. On this
large farm plenty of capital and experienced management
have resulted in more labour being employed than on
the separate farms, because there is a more intensive use of
the land, not only for cropping, but in the amount of live-
stock, cattle, poultry and pigs, all of which require labour.

In recent years there has been a considerable trek of
small family farmers from the Western counties and
from the lowlands of Scotland into the cheap arable
land of East Anglia and elsewhere. These immigrant
farmers were mostly specialists in stock-raising and dairying, and they have introduced a greater degree of
specialisation into the district into which they have moved.
Illustrations of this kind could be multiplied, but the
whole lot of them together, unfortunately, have made
little impression upon the hard core of agricultural distress.

They are indicative, however, of the initiative there is within the industry and point the way for future developments, if we can make them possible.

The Family-Farmers and Smallholders are mostly specialists in dairying, stock-raising, market gardening, pig or poultry keeping. As a body they are much more numerous than the labour-employing farmers.

Out of the 347,158 agricultural holdings in England and Wales, 233,885 are of fifty acres or less, and two-thirds of them have less than twenty acres each.

The occupiers of these holdings, however, have often some other occupation than that of the cultivation of their holding. In some counties Professor Ashby reports[1] that half of those with the smaller holdings are so circumstanced. The numbers of those who are "farmers" in the sense that they depend entirely on their holding for a living is probably less than half of the total number of the holdings of all sorts under fifty acres. All these holdings put together, however, only comprise one-fifth of all the land that is reported as being under crops or grass.

Those who are solely dependent on their holdings have a life of ceaseless toil. With the utmost frugality and industry they have struggled through bad times with relatively few casualties. The extent to which smallholdings should enter into any planned scheme of agricultural development is one of the most difficult problems we have to consider. For the present, however, we are concerned with the general features of farmers as a class, but in the matter of Sales and purchases the smallholders are, if possible, worse off than any other food producers.

As a skilled cultivator and producer the British farmer is hard to beat; but as a salesman he is deplorable. He tolerates, and even seems friendly to a system that "diddles" him out of his fair dues from January to December; and the smallholder is in the weakest position of all.

[1] Prof. A. W. Ashby, *The International Labour Review*, March 1935.

As I was getting together the material for this chapter, a neighbour happened to tell me of an experience he had just had. He is an industrious man who grows excellent vegetables that he sells himself as best he can. Being dissatisfied with the usual methods of sale he managed to obtain a stand for a stall in a neighbouring market town. He soon discovered that he could sell more from his stall than the produce of his own plot so he had to go afield for additional supplies. By driving sixty miles he found that he could obtain excellent fresh vegetables and fruit at a Warwickshire market town. One week, during August 1937, he bought a supply of "pots" of Pershore plums (70 lbs.) in excellent condition, fresh from the grower. They were sold one week at 1s. per "pot" of 70 lbs. and the next week at 6d. They were good sound plums and he could sell all of them at his stall. On one of these days the auctioneer, pointing to some crates of cabbages said: "How much for these?" My neighbour bid 1/-. Nobody else said anything and he found himself the possessor of five crates each containing about three dozen good cabbages, for one shilling! The crates alone cost the grower 3d. each so that he was out of pocket by 3d. on the crates alone.

This is what happens, not exceptionally, but every day in some market or other throughout the country. How can we describe a system of this kind? Think of the man who had toiled early and late to plant those cabbages, to clean the ground, to keep it free from weeds, finally to cut them, pack them in crates and send them to the market. At the end of it all he received 3d. less than nothing for his trouble.

The poor man, I expect, worked all the hours of daylight but he would be hard put to it to pay his bills, let alone getting a new suit of clothes now and then or ever having a holiday with his wife.

Can we imagine a manufacturer of boots or blankets, motor-cars or cigarettes, entering into large-scale production and sending his goods to be sold with a lottery like this in front of him? But this sort of thing occurs every day and has been doing so for years and years. The farmer grumbles at the Government or the weather and sends deputations to the Minister to ask for tariffs, for restriction of supplies or something of that kind, but it does not seem to occur to him that there is something under his nose that is worse either than the Government or the weather, and that he, as an isolated individual, is helpless against it, and hasn't an earthly chance until it is altered.

There has grown up round the sale of the farmer's produce, and more or less with his acquiescence, a vast and exceedingly powerful parasitical system which feeds on him. We shall have a good deal to say about it later on, and on the best way of dealing with it, but the point here is the attitude of the farmer himself towards it. A day once a week at the market is a very acceptable break in the week and provides a convenient, and often the only, opportunity of exchanging notes with friends and acquaintances. In the old days the sale at a local market was a convenient and practical way of disposing of supplies, and may still be for some purposes if we make the conditions sensible, but the world has altered since those early days of marketing. Great industrial cities have grown up. Bulk transport of supplies from all parts of the world goes on by day and night; arrangements are controlled, and often the prices also, by great or-ganisations which command the most skilled services, and the telephone carries their instructions throughout the land. Nevertheless the farmer still looks on, often with a friendly smile, whilst he knows that the dealers are meeting in the pub. across the road to arrange what sort of bidding they will engage in today.

The farmer asks for a dependable price system as a necessary condition of doing his work well, and rightly so. But it is as certain as that the sun will rise tomorrow that you cannot base one on a system like this.

As a Producer he is a man who can stand up against the world. In the market and in the price-rings amongst which he tries to sell his goods, he is as weak and helpless as a child.

PART I

SECTION III

Chapter IV

The Labourer[1]

His Skill and Disposition—His Historical Background—His Migration
to the Towns—The Causes—Low Wages—Long Hours—Poor Home
Conditions—The Labourer's Wife—Discouraging Outlook.

THE BRITISH FARM labourer is a skilled workman.
Let anyone who questions the truth of this try his hand
at the different jobs he has to undertake throughout the
seasons. Each one of them requires practice and knowledge
and, some of them, much skill. I know no other occupation
which is so diverse in the demands it makes upon a man.

He is tolerant and good-humoured, far shrewder and more
observant than many suppose, and his fortitude is amazing.
But if we are to understand his frame of mind and his probable response to the opportunities that may be created for him,
we must go back in history, because history has laid a heavy
hand upon him and his present attitude is derived from it.

He has been perhaps too tolerant, too acquiescent in
being poorly paid and badly housed, but history furnishes
the explanation. The events of the late eighteenth and
early nineteenth century led to a servitude from which
there seemed to be no escape. They had such a deadening
effect upon him that he accepted his position with despair,
and derived what comfort he could from the hope inspired
by the movement of John Wesley and others, that things
would be better in the next world, as it was manifestly
beyond his power to alter them in this.

Before the Enclosures of 1760 and onwards, although the
countryside was dominated by the squire and the parson,

[1] My thanks are due to Mr. H. B. Pointing, Editor of the *Land Worker*,
of the National Union of Agricultural Workers for much of the material
used in writing this chapter.

each man, as he grew up, could look forward to a cottage that gave him a right on the Common and to a strip of land which he could cultivate for himself. There was a degree of independence and self-respect in the villager's life which we have not yet succeeded in re-establishing.

Compulsory enclosures took his land and his rights away from him. As Hammond[1] puts it, the village classes and interests were scattered by enclosures: "It was not one generation alone that was struck down by the blow . . . the peasant with rights and a status, with a share in the fortunes and the government of his village, standing in rags, but standing upon his feet, makes way for the labourer with no corporate rights to defend, no corporate power to invoke, no property to cherish, no ambition to pursue, bent beneath the fear of his masters, and the weight of a future without hope."

By this policy, as Hammond truly said, the Government destroyed the spirit of a race. Their economic independence was gone; they were forced to accept a miserable wage supplemented by relief in kind, so that the meshes of the Poor Law spread over the whole country. Cobbett's appeal to the vestry of Bishops Walthams[2] for a scrap of waste land for the labourers was refused on the ground that it would "make the men too saucy", that they would "breed more children", and would "want higher wages". The Settlement Laws of that time also made it almost impossible for a man to escape from his village and find work elsewhere, and the Game Laws and the Trespass Laws made transportation the price of killing a rabbit.

It is almost impossible nowadays to imagine the cruelty of the governing class of that time when labourers were hanged for trivial offences, and little boys sentenced to transportation. The terror of human suffering was used as an instrument to force a new system upon the people as it has been in these days by Dictators. But the memory

---

[1] *The Village Labourer*, J. L. and Barbara Hammond, Longmans Green & Co., pp. 103 and 105.

[2] Loc. cit., p. 159.

of those terrible times sank deep into the minds and lives of the labouring population. It has influenced their talk to their children, and their whole attitude on life; the subservience and the fear of self-assertion that it engendered have continued like a blight from generation to generation.

It is far more widespread even now than many suspect—and sometimes with good cause. Those of us who go about in country districts know this only too well. This apprehension, coupled with reluctance to spare even a trifle out of his small wages, is the biggest obstacle of all to the labourer joining a Trade Union. I have met many wide-minded farmers who deplore it and know how much better it would be for the industry and how greatly it would add to its power, if all the workers were in their Union; but fear is still prevalent. Often, no doubt, an unsubstantial fear—but still, fear.

An incident occurred to me not long ago whilst on a speaking tour for the Labour Party in Cornwall that is worth recalling. On our way to a town meeting we arranged to call at a little village where there had never been a Socialist meeting before. We found a good company assembled in the street outside a door, which opened on to a stair, leading to an upper room where the meeting was to be held. They crowded round us to tell us in whispers that "The Lady is here. She has gone up!" We encouraged them to come along, which they did.

Upstairs we found a portly lady and a companion seated in the middle of the second row of chairs, and not another soul in the room. The villagers crowded in after us. The lucky ones put their backs against the far-end wall and the rest squeezed in front of them until the company filled the room except for a row of chairs which they left vacant behind the two ladies.

I stated our case as well as I could, and did not water it down either. At the end the Lady enquired "could she ask some questions?" I replied "certainly". She then asked a few of the usual questions which were quite easy to reply to, and after some closing words we rose to go. The Lady came up to me and asked "could she shake hands with me?", which she did. She said she had never heard our case before. She was very interested in it, and so on. Then suddenly she exclaimed, pointing to the villagers who were standing watching the scene: "But what do you think you will be able to do for these people? Look at them; they are afraid of me. Of an old woman like me." I could only say that perhaps she herself might think over why they were afraid: I was only a stranger. It was a significant incident. The barrier between fear and liberty is sometimes frailer than the fearsome suppose.

The self-confidence that is wanted will not arise under a system of well-meant patronage of the coals-and-blankets order which you still meet with in some places. It can only come from giving the people a decent chance in life in their own village. The greatest cause of the drift from the village that has been going on for a long time past, and especially since the war, is the feeling of the young men and women that they may have a better chance somewhere else.

In a country like ours, especially in these days of the motor bus, of the wireless and other apparatus of modern life, you cannot maintain a different standard of life between the good workman of the town and of the country. If the village worker is dissatisfied he will get away if he can; anyhow his son and daughter will. The more alert and enterprising a young man is, the more likely is he to do so. How far this movement of the more enterprising away from the land during the last fifty years has affected the quality of the stock left behind, I cannot say. Nature has a strange knack of reasserting herself in the long run; but it must be important.

This competition between the town and the country has been illustrated during the recent industrial revival. The average fall in the number of land workers for some years prior to 1935 was about 15,000 a year, but in 1936 it suddenly jumped up to 35,000. It was the attraction of the better wages that could be got in the factories of the neighbouring towns and the ability of the country worker to get jobs, despite the fact that in this time of so-called prosperity we still have a hard core of a million and a half unemployed. As a result there is already an outcry in some districts about the shortage of skilled farm workers.

Apart from the armaments programme, which I was recently told has "skinned" the farms in some districts, there seems to be no substantial difference of opinion as to the main causes of the movement from the land. A short summary of them will be useful.

The introduction of machinery and of changes in the methods of production that economise labour, account for the fact that, notwithstanding diminished manpower, the total home food-production, in one form or another, has been maintained—although we have lost nearly three million acres from arable cultivation since 1921.[1] A part of this loss is represented in the increase of grass, the rest has disappeared into "rough grazing". The increase of grass for stock-keeping has gone on alongside the growing labour shortage—partly a consequence of the scarcity of labour, partly a cause of it—but the records of the productive capacity both of the labourer and of the farmer, notwithstanding the loss of land, only make the more evident what we are losing in this disastrous business. The volume of output per man has increased by 25 per cent since 1921 and the Reports of the Cambridge University Farm Economics Branch estimate that on 1936 prices the value of his output increased by 50 per cent. In a critical examination of this case Professor A. W. Ashby[2] concluded that the output per agricultural labourer was "probably higher in England than in any other country in Europe". This is the sort of skill we are losing!

The loss is particularly affecting the younger men. Where there were 100 employed who were under 21 years of age in 1921, there were only 73 in 1931,[3] and the figure has become smaller since then. The corresponding fall for the older men was from 100 to 93, so that, before long, unless our policy alters, we shall have the industry increasingly dependent upon older workers with its inevitable results.

[1] For details of changes in Land Cultivation see Appendix II.
[2] *The International Labour Review*, March 1931, p. 323.
[3] Prof. Ashby, loc. cit., p. 334.

On July 27th, 1937, the *Farmer and Stockbreeder* published
a collection of letters from responsible and experienced
farmers on the causes of the labour shortage on farms.
They were unanimous as to the main causes; low wages,
long hours and bad houses. Let us look at these and
some other conditions of village life.

Previous to the war, after infinite struggles by their
trade union representatives, agricultural workers' wages
had gradually risen from 15s. a week at the beginning
of the century to 18s. a week. During the later period
of the war, after the passage of the Corn Production
Act of 1917, wages rose rapidly.[1] In 1918 they were
30s. 6d.; in 1919 37s. 10½d.; and 46s. 10½d. in 1920.

Then came the Repeal of the Act in 1921 and the fall
was catastrophic—to 36s. 10½d. at the end of 1921, then
to 27s. 10d. in 1922. Some of the fall was properly attributable to the fall in the cost of living, but the loss in wages
was far greater.

During the years 1918–21, notwithstanding the high
cost of food, the standard of life of the farm-worker was
probably higher than it had ever been. The repeal of the
Corn Production Act did more than depress the farm-
worker's wages—it destroyed his confidence and brought
back his old hopeless outlook. The agricultural Wages
Regulation Act of the Labour Government in 1924
arrested the decline and wages slowly recovered to 31s. 8d.
in 1931. They receded a shilling during the slump but
regained the 31s. average in 1934 and remained thereabouts until the end of 1935. During that year they varied
from 28s. 6d. in the lowest paid counties to 37s. 6d. in
the best. Since that time, and especially during 1937, there
have been increases in nearly all countries of from one to
two shillings a week, although at the end of 1937 there
were still more than a dozen counties in which 32s. a week
was thought to be sufficient for a working week of from
52 to 54 hours in the summer and from 50 to 52 in winter.

It is to be noted that these recent increases are con-

[1] I am indebted to Mr. Pointing for the following particulars.

siderably less than the increase in the cost of living during the same period, and many of them have been obtained only after the most unseemly wrangles on the County Wages Committees, by the votes of the Independent Members. The more enlightened leaders of the farmers are doing their best to abate this sort of thing and are meeting with some success, and the letters to the *Farmer and Stockbreeder*, already referred to, are encouraging evidence of a better disposition. The trouble is that the mischief has already been done. For years past farmers' spokesmen on ages Committees and elsewhere have resisted increases of wages, sometimes in very unfortunate terms, and the bitterness these proceedings have engendered has had a good deal to do with the resolve of the young men to get away from the land if they can. The short-sightedness of this sort of thing is self-evident. At the same time it is right to say that the biggest obstacle to obtaining a decent and reliable standard of wage is the uncertainty, and often the unfairness, of producers' prices.

Standard Wages are paid for Standard Hours, but these do not by any means represent the hours worked. In most cases the arrangements cover much longer hours. Merioneth and Montgomery seem to have the odious distinction of being the worst, paying 32s. 6d. for a week of 60 hours; but there are many counties in which 40s. a week or less is paid for a 60-hours week. This is the case in Cumberland, Gloucestershire, Hereford, Kent, Lancashire (north and eastern areas), Surrey, Denbigh, Flint, Glamorgan and others. In the Kesteven and Lindsey divisions of Lincolnshire waggoners receive 39s. a week for 61 hours in summer and 58 in winter. In the West Riding of Yorkshire 39s. a week is paid for the "customary hours" of 67½ in summer and 63 in winter. Christmas Day and Good Friday are holidays with pay in some counties, and in others Whit Monday and Boxing Day are included. In about half a dozen counties Easter Monday and August Bank Holiday have also been obtained, but, as the Report of the National Union of Agricultural Workers puts it, the struggle for these public holidays on farms is heavy going. Who can wonder that with a working week the length it is young men try to find a job in which they can have a few day-light hours to call their own.

Wages and hours affect the man as well as his family; but the state of the Home, the absence of domestic con-veniences, conditions at the village school and others like them, affect the mother particularly. The average cottage provided for the agricultural labourer is a disgrace. How the women carry on as they do and keep their children clean and decent and get the meals cooked, is a marvel. The extent of it is only realised by those of us who have taken the trouble to see things for ourselves. In the majority of cases, whatever the labourer or his wife may feel about their cottage, they dare not complain. They just put up with damp walls, no water supply, no drainage or conveniences, particularly when they live in a tied-cottage, as so many do. Happily, evictions from tied-cottages are not so frequent as they used to be, but when they do occur they have a lasting and disheartening, as well as a wide-spread effect. Everybody recognises that for some kinds of work, such as attendance on live-stock, a cottage at a suitable place is necessary, but such cases, as we shall see, need not prevent us from emancipating the farm worker from the thraldom which the tied-cottage so commonly imposes.

People cannot feel free to say what they think about long hours, poor wages, lack of milk for children, a leaky roof, a rain water butt that has given out and which compels the wife to go a long way down the road to a pond for every drop of water, when they know that their home is tied to their job and that if they lose their work their home goes with it. Often enough, no doubt, the workers' fear is unsubstantial; but it is there all the same, and it accounts for the question we are so commonly asked at meetings: "What are you going to do about the tied-cottage?"

The state of the village school, just as much as a dilapi-dated and inconvenient cottage, is a constant worry to the labourer's wife. There are many village schools where there are no means of drying the children's clothes in wet weather; where there is no place for the children to have their dinner when they have to take it with them, and where many more drawbacks provide anxieties for the mother. We see the lovely schools some of our towns and cities possess and scarce can realise what hundreds oɪ them are like in country districts. The state of the village school in this way is often a powerful addition to the disabilities of the country worker who has come to know what such things are like in towns.

In conclusion, what is the outlook for the labourer? He would prefer to stay in his village if he could be sure of a home there, which he could cherish as a home, and have good wages to support it, rather than migrate to a strange town. It is the place he loves. He knows his work also, and loves that too.

The proportion of agricultural workers who would prefer a smallholding to regular work under good conditions is not great, because they know the ceaseless toil the smallholding involves. For all that there would be more applicants for smallholdings than there are if the men felt, first, that there was a real chance of their obtaining a holding, and, second, a good prospect of success if they did. It is not an easy thing to get on to the list of "approved applicants" with some County Councils, and the fact that even of those who are approved, only one in seven gets a holding, keeps thousands from applying. Nevertheless the slender hope of ever becoming a smallholder is quite a minor reason for the movement from the country to the town.

The young Countryman, like other people, looks forward to having a home of his own and some free time in which to develop his pride in it; he wants to have something of the life that nature tells him might be his. But he has no chance. He is hemmed in by low wages and drab surroundings. He is cribbed, cabined and confined by a worn-out and short-sighted system.

Let us now examine the actual conditions of that system, beginning with the land.

PART I

SECTION IV

Chapter V

The Land

The Decline in Cultivation—Lamentable Condition of much Land—The Increase of "Rough Grazings"—Decline in Fertility—The Influence of Sport—Farm Buildings—Country Cottages—Lack of Drainage—Lack of Water Supplies—National Ownership Called For.

THE CULTIVATION OF our Land has been involved in a vicious circle for the past fifty years. Price slumps and land neglect have reacted upon one another and crippled progress. If the market for the sale of the produce of the land is freakish, uncertain and disordered it makes the producer hesitate to spend money on improvements and on maintaining the fertility of the land; and the more the land is neglected the more difficult it becomes to get a good crop out of it even if prices do seem promising. The one reacts upon the other. There has never been any national policy in agriculture. Standoffishness has been alternated by doles; but a Policy, never. It is time there was one.

It is not my purpose to go further back than is necessary or to burden the reader with many statistics, but some must be given. The outstanding facts are that since 1891 nearly four and a half million acres of useful land have passed out of arable cultivation, and nearly 300,000 fewer people find employment on the land notwithstanding the great increase of the population.[1]

Most of the land that was previously cultivated has been put down to grass; an increasing part of it is now described as "rough grazing" and has ceased to receive any sort of attention even as pasture land.

In looking out my notes I came across a passionately-

[1] For details see Appendices I and II.

worded memorandum on the subject which George Lans-
bury sent round to some of us in 1929 when he was dealing
with unemployment. "Idle land and idle men stare us in
the face", he said. "The most vital industry for any
nation in spite of State help of every description goes
from bad to worse. We talk of colonising other lands—
and our own land, so far as the countryside is concerned,
calls aloud for colonisation."

Our task in this chapter is to examine the facts so far
as the Land itself is concerned, in order to be able to
consider later what action should be taken. Those who
go about the country with their eyes open can see what
is happening easily enough, especially if they will take
the trouble to walk about the fields and farms even in
the districts where good farming might be expected.
Field after field may be seen with hideous crops of weeds,
reeds, thistles, nettles and brambles. The stock is very
scanty and the gates and fences and farm buildings are in
disrepair. In some parts of the eastern counties you can see
this sort of thing by the mile, and much of it on good land,
too. It is much the same on the good grass-land of the
Midland and South Midland counties, where hunting has its
Mecca. The most notable thing in that fine country is
the paucity of the good feeding stock the land ought to be
carrying. If you look closely you will find also a remarkable
absence of barbed wire to inconvenience the Hunt.

In his recent review of "Farming England", Mr. A. G.
Street sums up the case of these counties in these terms:—[1]

> "Still, such is the lamentable condition of the agricul-
> ture of the Shires generally that it seems that any
> change would be for the better, for the truth of the
> matter is that today scarcely one landowner in the
> Shires can live from his land, and that the farmers
> make a very poor living indeed.
>
> "Today the Shires appear to live on the money which
> is brought into them by wealthy townsmen and Ameri-

[1] *Farming England*, A. G. Street, p. 60.

cans who reside there during the hunting season, in order to enjoy the best hunting in all the world."

The Midland Agricultural College recently made a detailed report on this area of valuable land. Here is a typical sentence from their conclusion:—

"Today a competent observer would tour this area with growing depression. The farms, in general, are undermanned, undercultivated and understocked. Lime deficiency is almost everywhere glaringly obvious. Many of the water-meadows, costly projects of a century ago, are falling into disrepair and disuse. On some estates the carefully made roads and commodious farmhouses and buildings show only too clearly the effect of nearly a quarter of a century of neglect."[1]

This sober statement, with appropriate adaptation in form could fairly be applied to a large part of the farmland of the country. Whilst this state of affairs, in average cases, makes the case so bad, we ought not to shut our eyes to more extravagant examples of neglect.

Under any rational system we should have been spared the widespread desolation of the landscape that money-making has presented us with in the Potteries, Durham, and other districts where good land has been destroyed and a place made hideous that might have been beautiful. They represent the subjugation of agriculture. On the other hand the broken homes and rubbish-covered little fields of the Scottish crofts represent deliberate depopulation in the interests of sport, and not the failure of agriculture. The same can be said in other places. There is a particularly shocking place in North Hampshire where three thousand acres of what was once good farm land have been allowed to become derelict and the whole estate and its equipment to become an absolute ruin.[2]

Shocking as such examples are, however, we need not

[1] Loc. cit., p. 63.
[2] Details of this case were given by myself in the House of Commons, November 13th, 1930. *Hansard*, Col. 1897.

rely upon them to make a case. It is the general average that matters; and the result in them is not due to any ill-will or choice on the part of the owner or occupier; it is due to the break-down of a system. Mr. A. G. Street, himself a farmer, says:—

"The deplorable state of a large acreage of farming Britain today is enough to make one weep—land understocked, weeds flourishing, fences and hedges in disrepair, ditches and drains neglected, and everywhere a woeful lack of fertility, production and employment."[1]

This, without exaggeration, is the description fairly applicable to land we see in an ordinary way and which should be well supplied with live-stock or the scene of active husbandry.

There is another great area of land which we are tempted to disregard because we see little of it, except perhaps, during week-end rambles or holiday tramps. It comprises, however, nearly a third of the land of the country and the story of the neglect and declension of much of it that was formerly used, and which could be used again most productively, is appalling. We are indebted particularly to Professor R. G. Stapledon[2] for a dramatic presentation of the facts and for giving us in popular form the results of the researches which he and others have been conducting for some years past.

Reference has already been made to it as "rough grazing". There are more than fifteen million acres of it in Great Britain, and the land so described has increased by nearly three million acres since 1911.[3] After we have excluded all of it that is above the 1,500 feet contour, as well as all the land now devoted to grouse shoots and deer forests (which should not properly be excluded), we are left with some eleven million acres of hillside grazings or unused land above the 700 feet contour apart from

[1] *Farming England,* A. G. Street, p. 8.
[2] The Statements here quoted are taken from his recent book, *The Hill-lands of Britain,* Faber & Faber, 1937.
[3] See Appendix II.

more than four millions of rough grazings below that level. Formerly most of this land was used; and the ruined cottages or sheds that were once associated with an "intake" of a few fields that were cultivated and used in connection with the adjoining hillside grazing, are seen almost everywhere in our walks on the hillsides of Wales, Yorkshire, Scotland and elsewhere. As to how the disuse of this land has contributed to rural depopulation, apart from the evictions that have sometimes taken place in the interests of "sport", is strikingly illustrated in a case quoted by Professor Stapledon of 1,500 acres of land on the Carmarthen-Cardigan border. Formerly there were twelve cottage holdings on this land with some 600 acres of intakes and other land belonging to them. Up to 1904 from fifty-five to seventy children from these cottages used to attend the school. Now every cottage is in ruin, the whole land is treated as one holding, and the number of school-children upon it is four.[1]

It is not as if these rough grazings either above or below 700 feet were worthless. Far from it. They have been "let go" because we have never had either an agricultural or a land policy that encouraged or developed their use. Professor Stapledon tells us that the average production of meat per acre at present from rough and hillside grazings is from 5 to 15 lbs. per annum. For the hill farms associated with rough grazings it averages 14 lbs. At the same time he estimates that "very rough pastures" with periodic re-ploughing and re-grassing could yield 100 lbs. per acre per annum.

The extent to which neglect has gone in this disregard of our countryside is illustrated by the remarkable fact that the proportion of land actively cultivated or used as "tended grassland" is no greater in Britain than it is in mountainous Switzerland!

Up to this point the extent of Land neglect has been stated generally. It is necessary now to examine some of its attendant circumstances and results.

[1] Loc. cit., pp. 26 and 27.

There were two severe depressions in agriculture in the latter part of the nineteenth century; the one round about 1879, and the second at its worst in 1894. At the time of the earlier depression both landowners and farmers were still well-off and able to maintain the land and buildings in good condition, but by the time the second depression had reached its height this had ceased to be the case. Landowners more or less had given it up. Sir Daniel Hall sums up the attitude of the landowner in the 'nineties in these words:—

"In the main landowners had accepted the position that there was little future for farming, that the development of their estates did not offer an outlet for their energies or capital comparable to those available elsewhere, and that their function was to be easy with their tenants in return for the sport and social status that the ownership of land conferred."[1]

It so happens, however, that this period when landowners generally had lost heart, and many of them much money too, coincided with the commencement of the payment of Death Duties and there is no doubt that owing to the fact that Death Duties have to be paid in cash, and that the Treasury has never consented to receive land in lieu, they have been an increasingly potent cause of the almost universal cessation of the former contributions by the owner towards the maintenance of fertility and the provision of good buildings and equipment. The facts are not disputed by anyone who knows the case. They have passed beyond the boundaries of party political controversy.

Fertility

The gradual declension of land Fertility, owing to the absence of liming and manuring through a long series

[1] *English Farming, Past and Present*, Lord Ernle, 5th ed., Edited by Sir A. D. Hall, 1936, p. 387. Longmans Green & Co.

of years, was one of the most important difficulties which the Land Enquiry Committee of 1915 found that we were confronted with when there was an urgent call for more production during the war. The position has grown steadily worse since then. Under the land fertility scheme of the present Government (1937) the farmer is asked to provide three-quarters of the cost of the basic slag and half the cost of the lime. Whilst the more fortunate may be able to take advantage of this assistance, it is as certain as can be that it will not bring aid to the land that needs it most, simply because the farmer will not be able to afford his proportion of the cost. In a recent speech (August 1937) Viscount Bledisloe estimated that the fertility of the land could and should be raised by about 75 per cent. If this is anything like the case the losses we have sustained are even greater than many of us have ventured to suggest.

Sport

In this connection we should not overlook the contribution which sport has made to land neglect. The Land Enquiry Committee of 1915 drew attention to the influence which Game Preservation has exercised in causing declension in the use of land. A large amount of land, they reported, is withheld from its best use for the purpose of Sport, and a considerable amount has ceased to be cultivated at all because the owner can do better out of game rents than from farm rents. The Committee properly observed that a community seriously bent on making the best use of its land for purposes of food production would make every form of sport subordinate to the interests of the cultivator, and pointed out that whilst the large decline in rural population has been taking place, there has been an increase in the number of gamekeepers.

For all that, there are probably not more than 5,000 gamekeepers in the whole of Scotland. The amount of employment sport affords for a few days' shooting a year on the seven million acres in England and Scotland, now devoted to grouse shootings or deer forests, is trivial as compared with the labour that might be fruitfully employed if an intelligent use were made of the grazing possibilities of much of this land. It does not appear either that such a use need blot out either grouse-shooting or deer-stalking on much of this country. The number of cattle grazed on the deer forest lands of Scotland has declined by two-thirds even since 1920, and the number of sheep now on the same land is only 60 per cent of what it was at that time. As Stapledon put it: the incompatibility is not between the grouse and the sheep, but between the sporting tenant and the farmer, between the gamekeeper and the shepherd. The devotion of this vast extent of land to a monopoly for sport has meant the decay of industry, depopulation, and a denial of access the whole year round to multitudes of walkers who, under a well-directed system, would do no harm and derive much joy and restoration.

Buildings and Cottages

The position with regard to Farm Buildings over a large part of the country is dreadful. The reason is obvious. Buildings are expensive and few landowners and fewer farmers have the means to repair or replace them. Frequent reference has already been made to this subject and it need not be enlarged upon. It is enough to say that it is difficult to exaggerate the extent of the dilapidation, or the handicap it constitutes to good husbandry.

The case of the Country Cottage has already been referred to, but a little more should be said about it because the present Government still half-heartedly appears to regard the provision of cottages as a function of the landowner. Anyhow, except to a trivial extent it has not been accepted as a public responsibility.

In this connection it is appropriate, even to-day, to refer to the Report of the Land Enquiry Committee of 1915. That Committee came to these conclusions:—

1. That there is an urgent need in every county for more labourers' cottages, especially for those with three bedrooms.
2. That the condition of many of the existing cottages is most unsatisfactory and a considerable number of them are entirely unfit for habitation.
3. That there is a great deal of overcrowding.
4. That the unsatisfactory housing conditions are responsible for

   (a) A good deal of rural depopulation.
   (b) A serious loss of time amongst labourers who live in one village and have to work in another.
   (c) A general lowering of the standard of life.
   (d) A serious interference with the independence of the labourer.
   (e) Many young couples who desire to marry having to leave the district.
   (f) Sickness, invalidity, and the spread of disease.

They found also

5. That large numbers of cottages that were unfit for human habitation remained occupied because there was no other accommodation.

6. That 120,000 new cottages are required at the present time (1915) in England and Wales alone.

The Committee added also that not more than one in six of the cottages have a garden of more than one-eighth of an acre.

It is very doubtful whether the paltry provision of good cottages for farm workers that has been made since the war has kept pace with the increase of dilapidation of those which, although still occupied, are in fact unfit for habitation.

The surveys that have recently been made into overcrowding afford ample justification for this last remark, although the definition of "overcrowding" that is used automatically excludes many country cottages that are unfit for habitation. The Northamptonshire survey condemned more than 5,000 cottages outright out of 25,400 that were examined and reported that a large proportion of the rest needed reconditioning. In the New Forest out of 700 cottages examined 255 were found to be entirely unfit for human habitation and 208 others needed reconditioning. A Leicestershire farmer recently put it worse than that. He said that half the pre-war cottages needed to be destroyed and the rest required repair and reconditioning.[1] In Retford (Notts) the clerk reported that if they acted on the Medical Officer's report they would condemn about 80 per cent of the cottages.

Instances of this sort could be multiplied easily. They make it certain that the number of bad cottages is so great that the efforts so far made have made little impression. Some 34,000 rural cottages have been provided under the Housing Acts of 1931 and 1934, but it is probably an outside estimate to suggest that as many as 20,000 of them are occupied by agricultural workers. They cannot afford the rent.

Few acts of the present Government are more shortsighted or more deserving of censure than their stoppage of the provision of houses for rural workers under Mr. Greenwood's Act of 1931. We are not, however, concerned at this stage with the remedies but only with the facts. No figure less than 250,000 would suffice to give Agricultural workers the standard of home conditions that ought to be provided.

Drainage

A word of explanation is necessary if we are to understand the present position and what is required about Drainage.

Main or Arterial Drainage consists in keeping in good order the chief watercourses, including the rivers, so as to make them competent to carry the water coming into them from their tributaries, or that may be pumped up into

[1] Report on Rural Housing. The National Union of Agricultural Workers, October, 1936.

them from channels bringing water from surrounding lands that are at a lower level than the main stream. The responsibility for thus maintaining the main rivers and their tributaries belongs to the Catchment Area Boards (one for each river) which were set up under the Land Drainage Act of 1930. Subordinate to the Catchment Boards in certain districts are Internal Drainage authorities which have similar responsibilities for the main land drains.

These authorities therefore are already provided for, and their work could be done if the money were found to do it with. The dangers of the floods which occurred some months ago in the Fen Districts, where some 400,000 acres of the best land in England were in peril, were due to the fact that for years past the Treasury has been squabbling with the Great Ouse Catchment Board as to the amount of Government assistance that should be afforded. The result is that the necessary schemes for rendering the district safe, which had been prepared in detail years ago, have not been proceeded with except for trifling portions.

Neither the landowner nor the farmer are responsible in those matters, but they are responsible for what is known as Field Drainage. This consists of keeping the farm ditches or drains clear, and of the provision of drains on the fields themselves to carry the water from the land to the ditches. Both kinds of drainage are necessary, and in order to be efficient, must obviously be complete. If the land drains are not put in, or kept in order, the water remains stagnant on the fields and the land gets waterlogged—as will equally be the case if the ditches are not kept clear. Moreover, if one farmer keeps his ditches clear and the one below him does not, the same stagnation occurs. In the same way waterlogging or flooding occur if the main drainage is not adequate and, in such cases, the more efficient the land drainage is, the greater becomes the likelihood of flooding. Indeed, the situation at present in many districts is that if the farmers or owners could afford to carry out efficient field drainage their work would largely be stultified by the inadequacy of the main drainage system. If this obvious fact could be got into the heads of the Powers-that-be we should make more rapid progress with Main Drainage. For all that, land must get water-logged unless field drainage is carried out, however adequate the main drainage system may be.

Nearly four and a half million acres of land—and most of it good land—depend for their fertility and adequate use upon Main Drainage—or about one-seventh of the total acreage of English farm-land. Nearly two million acres of that land suffer from flooding because of deficiencies or obstructions in the main channels.

There are no reliable figures as to the precise area of land that is in need of restored field drainage, but it is safe to say that it must be millions of acres. Everywhere one goes, even in many cases where the land is not low-lying, we see evidence of the need of field drainage in tufts of reeds and soggy patches. In the Eastern counties, in many parts of the area of the Yorkshire Ouse, in Somerset and elsewhere, you may see this sort of land by the thousand acres.

For several years past on most of this land there has been no field drainage of any kind. The old land drains have become clogged up and useless, and neither owners nor farmers have been able or prepared to bear the expense of restoring the old drains or putting in new ones. Small grants have been made for some years past on a 50 per cent basis to farmers or owners to assist in field drainage; and from 1937 onwards an extra £140,000 was made available. The amount of work that will be done on this basis is trivial. As compared with the prodigious acreage of useful land which urgently requires field drainage, a method of this sort is rather like trying to eat a rice pudding with a pin.

Water   Supplies

So far as farm Water Supplies are concerned, agriculture is dependent almost exclusively upon ditches, ponds, or wells except for occasional pumping plants that have been installed by the owners.

EA

The grants that have been made under the Rural
Water Supplies Act of 1934 are practically confined to
household needs and only 2,300 out of our 12,860 parishes
had been assisted up to October 1936. Even in these cases,
so far as information is available, a large proportion of
the cottages are still without a piped supply.

There has never been any concerted effort to consider
farm or agricultural requirements. A large part of the
drier Eastern counties is half-sterilised, so far as the full
use of the land is concerned, by a deficiency of the water
supplies for the stock it might carry. An indication of what
the water supply requirements of a farm are may be
gathered from the simple fact that the allowance per milking
cow per day should be 25 gallons. Modern pig keeping,
even poultry keeping, requires large quantities of water
daily throughout the year; and no producer in a district
exposed to drought where adequate water supplies have
not been provided, can possibly expand his enterprise in
livestock keeping. The best that can be said on the subject
of farm water supplies is that, in many cases, farmers or
owners have made heroic efforts to provide for themselves,
but there never has been even a survey of requirements,
let alone any considered effort to provide them.

I need not extend further this review of the deficiencies
the land suffers from. This is how Orwin puts it:—

> "The crying need of the land is for fresh capital,
> for land drainage, for rural housing, for water supply,
> and for all the equipment that the landlord in the
> golden age of farming was able and ready to supply."[1]

How is the need to be met? Clearly the farmer cannot
meet it. Apart from the fact that he has not the means,
many of the things that require to be done, if they are
to be done sensibly, like drainage, water and electricity
supplies, are beyond the scope of an individual occupier.
The landowners, as we have seen, have given it up. It

[1] Orwin, *The Future of Farming*, p. 131.

can only be the State. The method adopted must be just to the parties concerned; it must be practical and appropriate to the needs of the case, but there is no other solution.

Happily, the recognition of this fact is no longer a Party matter. In our characteristic British way it is now accepted by men in all political parties as the only way of doing the job. The position, otherwise, has become impossible. In *Farming England* Mr. A. G. Street expresses his mind in these words:—

> "More and more I find myself being forced to consider this problem (land nationalisation) and more and more I am becoming convinced of two things in connection with it. *Firstly* that the nationalisation of the land of Britain is not so very far away; and *secondly* that it is the only thing which can provide a workable solution to the land problem of this country in all its aspects."[1]

He quotes an agricultural friend as saying:—

> "I don't care what they do or how they do it so long as this neglect of our lovely land is brought to an end. . . . If only I can drive through my own countryside without feeling ashamed of its farming. I don't care a damn what it costs to affect this; I am sure that the outlay would pay the nation tenfold."[2]

The friend may have been letting himself go in the last sentence but his case is unquestionably sound. We are confronted with a great task, and it has to be dealt with in a practical and wide-minded way.

The essentials of a good land system and the ways and means of achieving them must be considered later; but before coming to them, this review of existing conditions must be extended to cover the present inadequacies of distribution and the handicaps the producer suffers from in disposing of his produce.

[1] A. G. Street, *Farming England*, (Batsford, 1937), p. 6. My italics.
[2] Loc. cit., p. 8.

PART I

SECTION V

Chapter VI

Farm Produce and How it is Sold

Good Crops and the Producers' Poverty—Local Surpluses—National Surpluses—Market Prices—The Beef Subsidy—Local Markets —Distribution Costs—The Case of Milk—Seasonal Surpluses and Unregulated Supplies—The Case of Eggs—Difficulties in Changing Production—The Effects of the Present System.

"WE MUST PRAY God to send us half crops in future or we shall be ruined." So wrote a capable and up-to-date fruit-grower to me in a letter last year. It was a correct presentation of the ridiculous position into which we have drifted. It was reported on the wireless one week in September 1937 that the chief West of Scotland Herring Fishery Fleet was not putting out to sea, although excellent shoals of herrings were reported to be near, because the day before the fisherman had not been able to sell the whole of their catch and had dumped a part of it back into the sea. All the time, of course, there were lots of people who would have been glad of a herring for breakfast and multitudes of little children who had had to fill up instead with bread and margarine, and the fishermen themselves would have been glad to go out and catch more fish.

The fruit-grower with his apples and the fisherman with his herrings were in the same position as the unfortunate grower of cabbages referred to in Chapter III, and as thousands of other food producers are at different times throughout the year. They live under a dispensation which, as I have already said, "pays the producer as little as possible and charges the consumer as much as possible" and even seems to take a pride in the exploit.

There is no machinery whatever for relating the production, sale and marketing of food either with the needs of the people or with those of the Producer. It is left to the arbitrary operation of a system which depends upon the "private enterprise" of its agents to do the best they can for themselves.

The purchasers of fish at the port had in front of them more fish than the customers to whom they ordinarily sent their supplies, could take. There was no other way of disposing of the catch except through themselves; and they knew it. It would have been "bad business" therefore from their point of view if they had bid a penny more than was necessary to get them the fish they required. The rest went back into the sea. The fact that the price paid disgusted the fishermen and prevented them from going out next day to catch more fish, did not enter into the account. It was no affair of the fish purchasers.

I suppose the effect was similar with the unfortunate man who sold his cabbages for less than the crates cost him at Stratford-on-Avon market. He could not cart them back home. If he had known that this was to be their fate he would never have sent them. But there they were. It was not within his province to know that the cabbages that he sold for a quarter of a farthing each would be retailed a few hours later at twopence-halfpenny each, and that many a housewife who might perhaps have liked two cabbages for her family bought only one, and that many who would have liked one went without altogether, because they felt that twopence-halfpenny was more than they could afford to pay. All the market gardener knew was that it was hopeless to use his land for growing cabbages and that to expect him to pay rates and taxes and to live decently if this was the "raw deal" he was to be exposed to at the finish, was nonsense.

Cases of this kind occur regularly when a supply is sent to a local market, that is more than the purchasers present are able to take for their usual customers, just as they do whenever there is an abundant crop of seasonal produce such as fruit. Apart also from any local excesses in supply, the fall in price is always out of proportion to the increase in the supply. A small increase in supply may produce a large fall in the producer's price.

In addition to the effect of national or local surpluses, changes in producers' price are often determined by the dealers' rings which our present market system not only encourages, but places in a key position. Anybody who attends a local market knows well enough what goes on. In practically all cattle markets, for example, there is a close understanding amongst the dealers who are accustomed to attend. Not only do they refrain from bidding against one another, but often enough they arrange the scale of bidding and one of them buys for the group, and they share out afterwards.

An excellent illustration of the result of this sort of thing was afforded at the time of the introduction of the Beef Subsidy in September 1934. The subsidy consisted of the addition of five shillings per hundredweight to the price made in the market of good-class cattle. For seven weeks prior to its introduction the average market price was 40s. 3d. Directly the subsidy came into operation, down went the prices bid and the average price for the next seven weeks was 35s. 7d. Prices had been rising a little before the introduction of the subsidy and the volume of supplies coming forward was practically unaffected by its incidence,—as, indeed, they could not be, seeing the time it takes to fatten cattle. Nevertheless, although the average price for the third quarter, ending September, was 37s. 8d. the price for the fourth quarter (including Christmas, when prices usually rise a little) was only 34s. 6d. It should be noticed also that whilst the wholesale price was thus reduced in the fourth quarter the retail price was not. It increased by a halfpenny a pound.

The farmers expected that they were going to get five shillings per hundredweight in addition to the prices prevailing when the subsidy came into operation, and there was a plaintive reminder of this expectation in the House of Commons a year later when the subsidy was renewed. One member explained that he was then only getting

34s. per hundredweight for good quality cattle, and that therefore when the five shillings had been added he was little better off than before. He wanted to know how it was. There was, of course, no mystery about it. It had disappeared in the lower level of bids that came into operation when the subsidy began, to the advantage of the dealers and their friends.

Under the Live Stock Industry Bill of 1937 the Government proposes to close down a certain number of smaller local markets, but the system is to remain. As I myself put it in the House of Lords in the Debate on the Bill. Instead of the dealers meeting in the "pub" across the road at Little Peddlington to agree on the level of bids they are to make, they will meet in the lounge at the hotel of Great Peddlington, but the result will be no different. Indeed it may well happen that their mutal understandings will cover a wider area of supply and therefore more cattle.

Those who are interested in this sort of thing should read the Official Reports that have been issued on our Markets and Fairs.[1] They will find a story of old standing arrangements and customs for the sale of the husbandman's product that affords an interesting glimpse into rural history. These local markets were the convenient, and often the only way in which the producer could sell his goods. They were appropriate enough before the days of telephones and modern market communications, of large-scale modern transport and cold storage whereby great centres of industry are supplied with food products in bulk from all parts of the world.

If the interests of agriculture had been an intelligent national concern many of these old marketing arrangements would have followed Queen Anne to her grave long since. They might, perhaps, have done so if the weekly market had not provided an occasion for a regular assembly of friends and neighbours from a wide district for a pleasant round of shopping and gossip.

[1] Report on Markets and Fairs, Part 1, General Review. The Ministry of Agriculture, 1927. Economic Series, No. 13.

The country town is interested in the preservation of many of these markets; but what I have said does not preclude their continuance under a proper system. The country town, however, will benefit by a prosperous agriculture all the time, and not simply on Market day. But, apart from legitimate local considerations, a multitude of dealers, jobbers and others have been wiser in their generation and much more up-to-date in their mutual understandings than the scattered producers who continue with pathetic faithfulness to send their hard-won products to them for disposal.

If the producer, either of cattle or anything else, is ever to be emancipated from this exploitation and to receive the value that should properly attach to his produce, he must be afforded the service of a well-managed system that will enable him to obtain it.

This brings me to the next feature of the present system that is a perpetual handicap to the producer. It is the inflation of price that takes place between the Producer and the Consumer. One Royal Commission after another has deplored it, but it is not diminished; on the contrary we are probably tighter gripped today by distributive organisations than ever before.

A single illustration will suffice here and the case of Milk is selected because it is the most recent subject of official lamentation.[1] The price of milk to the ordinary consumer is more than twice the average return to the Producer for all the milk he sells; and this increase of price takes place in a few hours as compared with the years of toil and trouble involved in producing the cow that yields the milk. The result is that milk is dearer here than in any other country in Europe and multitudes of children suffer from the lack of milk their parents cannot afford to buy. The producer in consequence has to sell nearly a third of his milk for manufacturing purposes at $5\frac{1}{2}d.$ a gallon;—a price at which it cannot possibly be produced, let alone provide good wages for agricultural labourers.

[1] Report by the Food Council for the year 1936, p. 14 et. seq. Published by the Stationery Office, 1937, Price 6d.

Anyone who has studied our present distributive system will have discovered that any attack upon the ransom it extracts from the people will have to be made upon one of the best entrenched and most powerful of all existing vested interests. But the attack will have to be made, and made successfully, if ever the people are to be properly fed and the Producer decently treated. It would have been my lot to introduce proposals on this subject in the Parliamentary Session of 1931–2 if the Labour Government of that day had survived, and we shall face the issues that are involved later on in this book.

The next defect in existing marketing arrangements that should be noticed is the influence of seasonally high prices upon public habits of consumption and, subsequently, upon producers' prices. The case of new-laid eggs provides a good illustration. They are scarcest about November and most abundant in April and May. They are usually sold by the 120 (the long hundred) and I find that the season 1933–4 presents a fair average. The price in November 1933 was 23s. 3½d. per 120; whilst the average price for April and May 1934 was 9s. 7d.

The public is willing, and quite properly willing, to pay more for reliable new-laid eggs than for other eggs, but within limits. In the dear season the retail price gets up to 2½d. or even 3d. each, but sales begin to drop before these prices are reached. When I was Chairman of the Reorganisation Commission for Eggs and Poultry some large retailers gave valuable evidence on this point. The high prices of the winter months make people lose the "egg-eating" habit. Instead of having an egg with a rasher at breakfast they go without; and they do not resume the habit until some weeks after the increased spring supply has begun to come on the market. There is a lag of about seven weeks. During that time this loss of the habit of consumption has the effect of exaggerating the stock of eggs on the market and the spring fall in price is accordingly altogether out of proportion to the increase in supply.

A rational arrangement for keeping prices more level at a fair figure would eliminate this factor—and incidentally would have prevented the ruin of a good many novices in Poultry farming.

This case is only mentioned as another example of what necessarily attaches to the present unordered system, but it is particularly instructive because the results are due to home conditions affecting the demand for a popular home-produced article. The fall in price was not caused by increased importation because the importation of eggs was about the same in the spring months as it had been in the winter. It will be necessary, later on, to examine in detail the ways and means of producing a rational and reliable price system which takes account of all supplies whether home-produced or imported, but, wherever the supplies come from, the producer at present finds himself confronted by a system of sale that is fairly illustrated by the examples that have been given and of which many more could be provided.

When a food producer is confronted by prices that make it impossible for him to continue his production and get a living, he cannot suddenly switch over to something else; nor can he cease production. In this respect agriculture differs from most other producing industries. When a manufacturer finds orders slowing down he can diminish production. When orders come in again the machinery that is still there can soon be restarted for production. Labour, of course, suffers, all the time in all cases, under our present system, but the capacity for production is still there in most industries.

It is not so with land. Cultivation must be continued in one form or other or nature will replace it by a crop of weeds that may entail a summer fallow of the land, with nothing at all being grown, before any sort of production can be resumed.

In the same way the Time Factor is a vital obstacle if the land cultivator wants to change his method of production. The fruit-grower cannot root up his trees and use his land for something else except at great expense and with a long wait before him. Men just hang on in the hope that it will be better next year, or that "The Lord will not send a good crop". The market-gardener, say, cannot suddenly turn to pig-keeping. He would most likely need additional buildings, and, even with that prolific animal, he would require a couple of years at least before he could have sorted out unsuitable sows and got a decent herd. Even more so is the time factor important with other kinds of livestock. A man cannot turn over in a few months from raising store cattle to milk production. Even if his land and buildings are suitable, it is a matter of years before, by careful selection and experience, he can get together a good milking herd which he can rely upon.

Nature refuses to be hustled; and the knowledge that a long time must elapse before any alternative form of production can be adopted is a standing obstacle to change.

These two reasons—the necessity for continuing production and the delay in changing its type, compel the producer to carry on somehow in nearly all cases. He cuts out any costs that he thinks possible, particularly wages and the employment of labour. He goes without lime and the artificial manure that he ought to have, and his fences and buildings go unrepaired. At the last perhaps he lets down his land to "rough grazing" and its fertility and productiveness of food per acre decline accordingly.

This is no fancy picture. It is the reality with which this country is presented over millions of acres of fertile land, and the foregoing, moderately stated, summary of the conditions attaching to the sale of home-produced food displays some of the chief causes of this desolation. We have tolerated them too long.

Whatever system we live under, the prosperity of a producing industry, and the ability to carry it on with efficiency, must depend upon what is realised by the sale of its produce. Under the present system the sale of the produce of the land bears no necessary relation to the value of the produce, or to the needs either of the producer or the consumer. We can neither expect, nor deserve, success unless we replace it by a system which carries with it certainty of satisfaction for the efficient producer—farmer and labourer alike—as well as the provision of abundant food for the people on just terms.

PART II
ACTION REQUIRED

PART II

SECTION I

Chapter VII

Introductory Review

The Needs of a Good Land System—Present Insufficiency of Food. What its Production would Require—The Land to be Made Fit and Available; Necessary Conditions.—A Living for the Producer; Necessary Conditions.—Consumers' Prices—Conditions of Price Management.

WE ARE NOW approaching the more difficult part of our task, for it is always easier to point out defects than to suggest remedies for them, and it may help if we try to present the chief considerations that have emerged so far in order that we may have before us a general view of what we ought to try to do.

Try and imagine what the expanses of wasted or neglected land would be like if they were properly used; and if the use of them were associated with the needs of the people. Not only would a vast amount of good and healthy employment be provided, but it would mean a real restoration of the countryside. How beneficial also it would be to the rest of the community if the charms of our landscape could be safeguarded from spoliation and yet made sufficiently accessible for the people to enjoy. But if results of this kind are to be obtained we must have a very different land system from the present one.

What should be the main functions of a good land system?

They may perhaps be summarised as follows:—

First, the productive powers of the land should be able to be fully used according to our knowledge of what the land is best suited to produce.

Second, the whole agricultural population, farmers and labourers alike, should be able to find contentment and prosperity as the rewards of good work and the system should be one that will afford ability a chance, however humble its possessor.

Third, our moorlands, woodlands, and landscapes should be accessible to the people for enjoyment and fresh air, so far as that is consistent with their proper preservation and use.

Science moves along so fast, and is, year by year, opening up so many new possibilities that it would be futile to try and conjecture what may be the land's ultimate capacity for production, but there is a manifest need of good working arrangements whereby the lessons of science may be progressively applied and their results made available to cultivators as they reach the stage of practical application. There is, however, plenty to be going on with in the light of the knowledge we already possess, for there are many things of which the people are in daily need, and for which our land and climate are unquestionably suitable, but which are not being produced in anything like the quantities they should be.

In this Chapter, therefore, I will try to present in a summarised form the chief requirements of the case as they affect (1) the Nutritional Needs of the People, (2) the Land itself, (3) the Producer, and (4) the Consumer, so that we may have the necessary background for considering the lines of action required for the Programme of Development that we might seek to realise.

Recent researches into the problems of Nutrition have revealed the glaring insufficiencies of our present scheme of food production as compared with the needs of the people.

It seems a far cry to the discussions of 1914 in which some of us took an active part, and which led to the first Exchequer grants for infant welfare. Even then the chief cause of the disgracefully high infant mortality of those days was proved to be defective feeding. I remember once making a suggestion which was received with some derision in official circles; it was that we ought to go in for a system of advertisement to the effect that "the proper food for a baby is milk, and nothing else". Just a slogan like that. Nothing more in fact than a truth which nature has been shouting at us since Eve had her first baby, but the neglect of which has been more responsible than anything else for the waste of infant life and for poor health amongst children. There is nothing high-falutin' about these things. They are nothing more than the application in a collective form of common knowledge.

At long last we are beginning to have the advantage of the results of official and responsible enquiries presented in such a form that they are helping to mould national policy. A responsible Body of Scientists in 1934 reported on the nutrition of the people to the British Government, and presented a series of recommendations. The precise form of their report was confidential, but there was never any secret about what most of them thought as they had all spoken publicly upon many occasions. The League of Nations also has its responsible Committee and has issued a series of most valuable reports, and others, like Sir John Orr, have put the case with challenging authority. There is no difference between any of them as to the main lines of their criticisms and recommendations. Let us apply them to our own population.

The Scientists reported that there were widespread physical defects of nutritional origin. An examination of the diet of the people showed that cereals in one form or another form about 60 per cent of the food the people consume, and the poorer the people the higher the proportion. Bread is, of course, well worthy of its age-long title "The Staff of Life", but man does not live healthily by bread alone. There is a great deficiency in the food of the people, especially amongst children, of what are described as "protective foods"—Milk, Butter, Cheese, Eggs, Meat, Vegetables, Fruit, and, to some extent, of Potatoes.

As the League of Nations Report puts it,[1] "the greatest single cause of defective nutrition in any community, is

[1] League of Nations, "The Problem of Nutrition". Vol. I, p. 77.

FA

poverty and the ignorance that is often associated with poverty". Or, as they say in another place,[1] "the nutritional adequacy of the diets of various groups of the population is mainly dependent upon their income".

We have only to look at the list of "protective foods" just mentioned to see that they are foods which we are particularly well able to produce in abundance in this country and that the purchase of them in sufficient quantity at present prices is beyond the means of millions of people.

We have become familiar with Sir John Orr's classification of the population.[2] It amounts to this: There are $4\frac{1}{2}$ million people who can only spend an average of 4s. a week on food and their diet is "inadequate for perfect health in all important constituents". There is another nine millions which can only spend 6s. a week on food, and their diet is inadequate in many of the chief protective requirements, and even in the next group of nine millions, who can spend 8s. a week on food, their diet is inadequate "in minerals and vitamins". These three sections of the population, numbering in all about 50 per cent, contain in fact more than half the children. Scientists tell us that after a child is weaned it should have at least a pint of milk and one egg yolk until it is twelve months old, and that after that age the average requirement of a child is $1\frac{1}{2}$ pints of milk a day up to twelve years of age in addition to eggs, green vegetables, fruit, etc.

When we find, in comparison of milk needs of these dimensions, that the average consumption per head, even including the well-to-do sections of Society, is not much more than a quarter of a pint per head per day, we get a glimpse of the need which has to be met. The case is not perhaps quite so glaringly deficient in some other foods, but it is within the truth to say that the people need an increase of at least 25 per cent in their consumption of butter and

[1] Loc. cit., p. 24.
[2] Food, Health and Income, Prof. J. Boyd Orr, Macmillan & Co., 1936, 2s. 6d.

eggs, and an increase of from 50 to 60 per cent in that of fruit and vegetables, apart from an increase of, say, 12 per cent in meat. There is, therefore, ample justification for the conclusion of the League of Nations Committee that

"There can be no doubt that the real interests of nations demand not a restriction of agricultural production, but the discovery of means whereby the real needs of each community for the health-giving foods may be correlated to the undoubted power of agriculture to produce all that is necessary for abundant health."[1]

We need a supply of milk, cheese, butter, vegetables, eggs, fruit, and, to some extent, of meat, that is far in excess of our present production. The folly of restriction of supply as a means of bolstering up prices is thus manifest, as is the similar folly of tolerating a distribution system which so inflates prices that it compels people to fill up their children with bread and margarine instead of giving them a fair supply of the other foods they need.

Later on I shall examine in detail the Programme of Production that would be involved if we set about making a proper use of our Land, but it may be interesting to express in Tabular Form at this place the results on present production if we were to produce the increased quantities of the Protective Foods referred to at home.

It must be understood that the figures related only to the increased quantities the people now need and takes no account of further home production in place of supplies that are at present imported.

On the basis of the National Consumption in 1935: If the people consumed 50 per cent more milk, 25 per cent more of butter, cheese and eggs, 50 per cent more fruit and vegetables and 12 per cent more meat, the result would be as follows:—

[1] Loc. cit., p. 87.

Increased **home** production required to meet the above:

per cent.

Milk	} Increased milk production required 100	
Butter		
Cheese		
Eggs		60
Fruit		78
Vegetables		60
Meat		25

The figures provide an illustration of what a planned development of agriculture should lead to; but in a matter of this kind, involving an expansion of Agricultural production and a corresponding increase in the purchasing power of the people, the pace cannot be quicker than the arrangements, that can be established as we go along, will provide for. It can only be done if we succeed in fashioning a system that will inspire confidence and retain public support as well as the co-operation of the cultivators.

To this end, so far as the industry itself is concerned, we must be able:—

1. To make the land fit and available for its proper use by good cultivators, and
2. Ensure for good cultivators the well-being and content they are entitled to.

The main necessities under these two heads should be taken separately.

The Land

There is clearly no way in which land may be properly planned for use and adequately equipped except under a system of National ownership. That system must include the ownership of all agricultural and open land. The expression "open land" is used because there are abundant reasons for taking land that is now waste or not used at all. Much of it may be suitable for afforestation and should be available for that purpose. We may be also certain that in the future the work that Professor Stapledon and others have been doing will bring much land, that is now entirely unused, into use for meat production. As a minor, but important reason, there are no other means whereby our national treasures in landscape, mountain, or coastland scenery may be safeguarded from the spoliations of the developer as well as obtained for proper public enjoyment and use. In this connection it is to be noted with what satisfaction even Conservative newspapers record the fact that the National Trust has secured possession of a piece of Dovedale, a farm on the slopes of Beeston Tor, a piece of the Lake District, a scrap of cliff or some other choice morsel. But what a pitiful business it is. No wonder it moves to anger so many lovers of our country, and that their sentiments find expression, as they do in Mr. Clough Williams-Ellis'book *Britain and the Beast*, and in the protests of so many others who are filled with despair at our present helplessness.

If the Land is acquired for the Nation it must be paid for. This case will be argued in the next Chapter; but, accepting that conclusion for the present as just in itself and as necessary, it is clear that the basis of payment (compensation) should be that of the fair value of the land and not of a fictitious value. If it can be obtained on this basis, what asset in the world can be better than the land of Britain? This means, however, that there must be a Body of Persons responsible for carrying out the work, and that they must work in close alliance with those who are responsible for making the equipment of the land what it ought to be.

By Equipment of Land we mean the provision of suitable buildings for the purposes of cultivation, the improvement of its Fertility, as well as adequate drainage and water supplies. Drainage and water supplies are engineering tasks, and will, to some extent, require special organisations for their execution, but it is evident that the direction of all the work must be a duty of a National Body. The improvement of fertility must be a joint concern of the National owner and of the occupier since much of it must be a part of the routine work of good cultivation.

The provision of cottages and other necessary parts of rural restoration will be dealt with separately.

Nobody but a fool would expect that we can "Farm from Whitehall". The requirements of the land depend upon the land itself; and therefore we must contemplate the necessary association of experienced management with suitable local agencies on which those associated with the industry itself will play an important part.

It must be clear also, even from the brief references that have already been made to the different types of husbandry and to the manifold industries that are included in the term "Agriculture", that we cannot contemplate any stereotyped or one-sided type of farming. Any system that is to be successful must invoke the good will of people who understand the business and provide opportunities for advancement of capable young men who do not happen to have capital. It should aim at helping and encouraging efficient tenant cultivators as well as providing for the adoption of new methods and for diverse types of farming. It will be necessary to plan future developments, often on a large scale, and for this reason I feel sure that large-scale operations both for mixed farming and for intenser methods of production will be called for. At the same time there will be a need, especially in some districts, for the encouragement of smallholdings on lines that will give the holder the advantages of organised management in estate work, sales, purchases and other matters in respect of which he is at present at a great disadvantage.

A Living for the Producer

Producers' prices present the most difficult problems of all. The prices also that consumers have to pay for food react, as we have seen, upon what the producer receives, but they must be treated separately.

Producers' Prices

The greatest bugbear of the farmer is *uncertainty* of price. Now and then, like eggs at Christmas-time, or when there is a half-fruit crop, producers' prices may be high, but he never knows what will be the state of affairs next year, less still the year after, whilst production implies planning for a year and often two years ahead.

Reliability of Price at a fair level must attach to the system we plan. The length of time over which the same price can be obtained must depend upon the successful development of the scheme, but our aim should be to obtain as long a term as possible. During some periods prices may be subject to variations but they should be made known in advance. The reasons for these variations will be referred to when we deal with different commodities, but as even a level of price as possible should be our aim.

Another factor that ought to attach to a sound price system should be the encouragement of efficiency in production; and, in this connection, the term "production" should include grading and packing, and presentation of the goods in a form acceptable to the market. That is to say better prices should attach to better qualities and better-presented goods. This feature of a sound system carries with it the necessity for organised arrangements for the distribution of market Intelligence and for advice in preparing to meet the needs of the market, because the convenience of the customer is the end in view.

Another essential concomitant of any satisfactory scheme must be that the benefits of the prices assured are passed on to all engaged in the industry. It would never do to provide a system of satisfactory prices for the farmer and still leave the labourer, or his representatives, to haggle and struggle for odd sixpences on County Committees. We must develop arrangements whereby they share *as of right*, and automatically, in the increasing prosperity that the system will bring as it gets into operation. This necessitates some important modifications of the arrangements that we have at present. For the moment, however, it suffices to point out that a consideration of these changes lies before us.

So far, what we have said relates to the prices that the producer will receive for what he *sells*, but it is impossible to expect that any scheme will be permanently satisfactory unless it takes account of the prices and arrangements that attach to what he has to *buy*. High prices of feeding-stuffs, for example during 1937, have been one of the greatest difficulties of the poultry and pig producer. There has been no sort of correspondence between egg and bacon prices and the prices of food-stuffs. In these cases where the cost of feeding is the most important, single, element in production the rapid rise in the price of feeding-stuffs, with little changes in the level of the selling prices, has dislocated the work of thousands of producers. It is obvious, however, that little can be done in this direction unless it is dealt with by a comprehensive and business-like organisation; but there is no reason to suppose that the fashioning of such an organisation would meet with the irreconcilable opposition of the big suppliers of these commodities.

Do not let us, however, pretend that a rational and well-conducted marketing organisation will not dispense with a considerable number of the swarms of middlemen, dealers, travellers and the rest, that the producer pays for at present, whether he knows it or not. It ought to; and it will. Not inconsiderately, or in any wholesale or reckless fashion, but it must do so in the end, and nothing is to be gained by failing frankly to face the fact. The arrangements for the passage of the producers' goods on to the market must be immensely simplified.

The Consumers' Price

Taking it all together the excessive difference that now prevails with many food-stuffs between what the producer receives and what the consumer pays, is a discredit to an intelligent community. But when we have said that we must not conceal from ourselves that in trying to diminish this difference we shall be confronted with powerful interests, and the struggle may be long and bitter, although that need not necessarily be the case if the problems are sensibly handled; but knowing full well the sort of Press campaign that can readily be organised, it would be foolish to enter upon this effort without recognising what may be in front of us.

We may take it for granted that no modification of present methods of distribution can succeed that leads to a stoppage of supplies of food even for a day. You cannot do anything that will leave London without its morning's milk, or Birmingham without its bread. Let us remember that.

There are other conditions which should attach to plans for improving distribution. They must take account, in a sufficient measure, of local variations in public habit and be accompanied by such a system of propaganda and information as will secure a public understanding of what we are driving at and thereby retain public support. The variation in food habit is infinitely greater than anyone might suspect who has not taken the trouble to examine it; and we have to recognise that there are few things in which the public is more touchy than in matters of this sort. It is true that many of these variations are wasteful in character and often involve the distributor in unnecessary expenses, but sensible direction must take account of them, for we must not lose sight of the fact that, in the long run, it is the woman with the market basket who controls the situation.

These preliminary considerations may perhaps seem trite, but they are so continuously important that I make no apologies for putting them in the forefront.

Machinery for Price Management

The management of any price system that may be introduced will have to be upon a Commodity basis or, in some cases perhaps, upon a grouped-Commodity basis. The channels of marketing and the methods of marketing

of many commodites are so different from one another that
no other system would be practicable.

Apart from this there is no way of securing reliability
in our price system unless at some point or another in the
passage of the supply either from the home producer or
from the port to the consumer, there is *control over the
supply*.

The methods of control and the machinery suitable for
the different commodites will necessarily vary, but no
system can be worked efficiently and smoothly unless we
plan our arrangements in such a way that control can
be exercised at some appropriate place. For example,
there is no way in which we could secure full and proper
payment for the producer for fat cattle except through a
publicly-controlled abattoir system. That is where the
cattle must come sooner or later; and the needless shiftings-
about, commissions for dealers, jobbers and the rest that
now intervene between the producer and the abattoir are
not only wasteful but make the administration of a sound
price system an impossibility. The abattoir, as you
might say, is the appropriate "bottle neck" in this case,
and others must be found or devised somewhere in the
marketing for all major food commodities. This necessity
will lead us to the consideration of the character and
functions of the appropriate Home Producer and Import
Boards and account should be taken of excellent lessons
available in what has already been achieved by different
trusts and trade combinations.

In conclusion, it should be said that the final control of
prices cannot be left to the interested parties. The public
will properly insist that their dominant interests are
safeguarded.

Our aim must be to provide the people with Plenty on
just terms, and at the same time enable the home producer
to make his contribution to the provision of that plenty
under self-respecting conditions.

PART II

SECTION II

Chapter VIII

The Acquisition of Land

Limited to Agricultural and Open Land—Past Proposals. Spence; Paine; The Taxation of Land Values; State Control without Purchase —Reasons against Confiscation—The Method Suggested. Preliminary Conditions; The Size of the Transaction; The Basis of Value; The Ordinary Landowner; Methods of Payment. The Owner-Occupier; Options Suggested; Mr. Davies's Proposals. Special Cases—Prospective Building Values—Leaseholds—Timber Plantations—Publicly-owned lands—Method of Transfer to the State.

THE PREVIOUS CHAPTERS bring us to the necessity of considering the ways and means of the acquisition of agricultural and open land.

The question of *how* it is to be done must be related all the time with *why* it is to be done.

Why are the proposals limited to agricultural and open land and not made for all land? The answer is that national ownership of agricultural land is required for its proper equipment and use so that the industry may be successful and the countryside prosperous. Any case that may be made for the acquisition of town lands, and especially for the almost priceless land of some of our cities, rests upon a set of considerations that are entirely different from those here being examined. It is a big enough job to consider what is necessary for a successful agriculture without allowing oneself to become entangled in the numberless questions and fierce controversies that would attach to the proposed national acquisition of *all* land. First and last our job in this book is agriculture, and what is necessary for its restoration and well-being. The case for the national acquisition of land for that purpose is unassailable and widely admitted.

At different times various methods, other than that of

outright purchase, have been suggested in order to secure the proper control and use of land, and some reference should be made to them.

Thomas Spence in 1775, in his lecture on "The Real Rights of Man", advocated a system of village or parochial ownership with the land controlled or managed by the village community. In effect the proposal was to institute a system of farming managed by the farmers of each village, each village community apparently operating as a separate unit. Proposals of this kind can only be supported nowadays by those who have no real or first-hand knowledge of the conditions which prevail in the many thousands of our villages. How it would be possible to obtain any common directions or common development in response to national needs by machinery of this kind, passes one's comprehension. One village perhaps would be well led; another badly led; the majority not led at all, each cultivator, as now, being a law unto himself. In one place, one type of production would be encouraged; in another, another, and in any case with these thousands of independent, or semi-independent, units it would be impossible to frame a system which would provide the modern equipment so badly needed, or give that reliability of price and efficiency in the marketing of the products which are vital to the prosperity of the industry.

About the same time as Thomas Spence wrote, Thomas Paine was advocating the appropriation of Land Rents, except those arising out of the owner's own improvements, for the establishment of a fund for starting young men in life and for giving assistance to people over fifty years of age. Paine wrote, of course, in the days when agriculture was the dominant industry and when landlords were dominant also. His proposals clearly have no relation to the condition of the world today.

The proposals of Mr. Henry George in *Progress and Poverty*—as represented to-day in the proposals of the English League for the Taxation of Land Values—are, however, still with us. Whatever may be said for the taxation of Urban Land Values, the proposals are ineffective when applied to agricultural land. In the current exposition of this system, *Land Values Taxation, the Essential Reform*, by Chomley and Outhwaite, 1909, we are told that Land Values are "the price of rent which could be obtained in an open market by land divested of any improvement which may have been made upon it". As soon as we apply this principle to agricultural land, what have we left? The ploughing and cultivation of the fields and the rooting up of briars and rubbish are improvements; fences, ditches, draining, manuring, are all improvements, and so are farm buildings, barns, cowsheds, stables and the rest. When the value of all these is ascertained (and one's heart is moved to pity for the man who is called upon to ascertain them), what have we left? A Prairie. There is nothing left to tax. Immense and costly valuations over years of controversy would lead to prairie values in the end. This, manifestly, is no way in which to obtain the control and use of agricultural land. As a matter of history, I may say that in the early stages of Viscount Snowden's Land Tax proposals for the Budget of 1930, it was proposed to include agricultural land, but a consideration of the case in detail compelled its abandonment.

There is one other alternative to State Purchase which has been seriously recommended, and detailed proposals with regard to it were put before me as Minister of Reconstruction in 1918. They represent, in substance, obtaining what is required through an extension of the Control system that was established during the war. At that time the County Executive Committees established under the War Agricultural Committee of the Ministry of Agriculture had very drastic and comprehensive powers. A recital of them will be found in the Cultivation of Lands Order that was issued in an extended form on March 15th, 1917. Under that Order the Board (now the Ministry), after consultation with the Food Controller "with a view to maintaining the food supply of the country", could do some very drastic things. They could:—

(a) Enter, and if need be, take possession of any land which, in their judgment, was not being adequately cultivated.

(b) For the same purposes take possession of any machinery, farm produce, stock or animals.

(c) Provide housing accommodation.

(d) Utilise any water supply or motive power for their purpose.

(e) Serve a notice on the occupier as to how he was to cultivate his land.

(f) If need be, determine a farmer's tenancy, and

(g) Arrange for the cultivation of the land by some other person.

A large number of Orders were issued by County Committees under these powers. Between them they entered into the possession of more than 23,000 acres of land, and they determined tenancies, either themselves or by instrucing the landlord to do so in some 250 cases. The operations of the Committees did, in fact, deprive the landowner of any effective power in regard to his land, and left him in the position of being no more than the receiver of a fixed rent.

That was the system to which we were driven under the stress of war, not twenty years ago, and there is little doubt that if, in the future, the nation should be presented with the calamity of war, a system of this kind would be introduced at an early date unless, before that time, we had been sensible enough to adopt the system of practical development under national ownership which it is my purpose in this book to recommend. It is difficult to believe that, short of the emergency of war, it would be possible to persuade our fellow countrymen to adopt an arbitary system of this kind, in the control over what is still regarded as "private" property.

There is, finally, one other method which may be mentioned and which all of us who have spoken on the subject have been confronted with at different times. It is represented by the question we have all had to reply to: "Why not take the land without paying for it?"

Behind this question there is sometimes a reference to the special nature of the private ownership of land and, more often, to the questionable means whereby some of it was obtained in times past. It is true that the private ownership of land confers upon its owner a power over his fellow-citizens which, when exercised, is greater than the power possessed by the owner of any other form of private property. We must live on the land; and if the power of the owner were absolute this might be made impossible. Because of this, land ownership has always been separately treated in law and the fiction established that land is held for the King. But, as we have seen already, the power of the private owner of agricultural land has come to be controlled or circumscribed in many ways by the different Agricultural Holdings Acts, as described in Chapter II.

So far as the questionable methods of acquisition in days gone by are concerned, how are we to distinguish the land that belongs to the descendants of some bad baron of old who very likely stole it, or to some land-grabber of the time of the Enclosures? Much of it now belongs to thrifty persons who have put their life's savings into the acquisition of some freehold or another, and more than nine million acres belongs to owner-occupiers—at least two-thirds of whom have had to buy their holdings within the last twenty years. It is true that in the vast majority of cases they would not have done so if they could have avoided it and thereby escaped experience of the truth of the saying that "there is no worse landlord than borrowed money".

Surely we are no more entitled to take these people's property without paying for it than we are any other kind of property. It is also a political certainty that the electors of this country will never consent to the confiscation of a private person's property honestly acquired, whether it is land, furniture, houses or anything else. Apart therefore from the morality of the case, political sense must make us recognise that if the land is to be acquired at all it must be paid for.

Those, also, who are interested in the probable results of a policy of confiscation are advised to read Chapters 56 to 61, Volume II, of Mr. Bernard Shaw's *Intelligent Women's Guide to Socialism*. Neither his frankest friend nor his worst enemy would ever accuse Mr. Bernard Shaw of an undue regard for the feelings of landlords, but in the Chapters referred to he sets out with characteristic pungency, but with unassailable logic, the fact that "nationalism without compensation would be catastrophic".[1] The defenders of the existing Land System, although it has led us into the present mess, could indeed ask for nothing better than that its opponents should advocate a policy of confiscation. They could then indeed sit back quietly and look on at the row. If land, why not railways, factories or anything else? Or, if it comes to that, the homes we live in? It would mean the mobilisation against us of the goodwill and interests of millions of people who want to see a successful agriculture and a prosperous countryside. If there ever was a case in which that somewhat unworthy maxim "honesty is the best policy" is in accord with good sense, it is this. Let us, therefore, agree that the land must be paid for and consider how and on what basis.

The Acquisition of the Land

The first thing to be said—and it should be borne in mind all the time—is that efficient and honest management is essential. This means that there must be a capable and experienced body of persons in charge of the business. Let us call it, for the sake of giving it a name, the National Agricultural Commission.

It is also to be remembered that the machinery must be ready when any transfer of land is made. We do not enlist recruits for the Army without having a War Department ready to train them, nor build cruisers without an Admiralty to receive them. If were Mines nationalised it would not be done by a simple stroke of the pen, but on some appointed day or days by which time a Mines Department would be

[1] *Intelligent Women's Guide to Socialism*, Bernard Shaw, Vol II, p. 272.

ready to assume its responsibilities. In the same way we should not take over land without a competent Land Department having been arranged for. Some readers perhaps may think these observations unnecessary, but we cannot make it too plain that Socialism is a sensible and realistic business.

There is one other important preliminary consideration. We should avoid cluttering up our machinery by responsibilities that are not essential, or by introducing needless complications into valuation or management. Our proposals should be limited by the objective before us—that is, confined to agricultural land. In that expression, as I previously explained, we include all open land, grouse moors, deer forests and the rest.

It should also be made clear, beyond peradventure, that the scheme should not include the acquisition of private houses, shops or residences, even in rural areas. Farm houses, and farm cottages as well as farm buildings, must, however, be included as they are essential parts of the industry.

It will be necessary to consider the amount of land which might claim to be exempted from purchase as attaching at present to private country residences, such as Park Lands, but apart from special cases of this type that will require to be dealt with fairly, the proper course is to include *all* land now dealt with as agricultural, even where it is included in Urban districts.

Thus defined: what is the size of the problem to be dealt with? What amount of money or "compensation" might have to be paid so far as we can presumably estimate?

The opponents of national purchase will try to keep their fellow-citizens awake at nights by attempting to alarm them as to the magnitude of the transaction. They will indulge in hectic talk about inflation amongst other things. There will be no inflation at all. The present owners of the land would simply exchange one form of security for another. The most careful and critical examination of this question that has hitherto been published in book form is that of Orwin and Peel in *The Tenure of Agricultural Land*. Their estimate of the value of the land

GA

of England and Wales—after they had made the generous allowance of an increase of 20 per cent on the rents received in the years 1921–2 and had estimated that purchase would be on the needlessly liberal basis of 22½ years—was £1,125 million.[1] In the latest officially published Report[2] on the Agricultural Output of England and Wales the capital value of the same land in 1931 was estimated at £645 million to which should be added £280 million for tenants' capital, making £925 million in all. This agrees very nearly with comparable figures that were provided for me when Minister of Reconstruction. At that time the value of the agricultural land in Great Britain, on a basis of 20 years' purchase, was put at about £1,000 million. The undertaking would necessarily be spread over a series of years, but the whole transaction would only amount to about two-thirds of what the country has recently undertaken without disturbance, in the provision of £1,500 million for armaments.

But what an asset would the nation be acquiring if it became the possessor of its agricultural land! Land is the only asset that improves with use. Shells and guns and battleships are rapidly wasting assets and so are factories and machinery, but land is there still—the better and the more valuable by sensible use—and this, moreover, is entirely apart from the improved values that would come to the National Commission from any buildings or town extensions that might take place upon it.

If the State had purchased the land, as some far-sighted men wanted us to do, at the end of the war, what handsome increments the Commission would have become possessed of by now! Its loans for development or improvement purposes would certainly have been more than covered by the increments of value that have taken place since the war, even when the most generous allowance is made for the restraint of operations of the "developer" which an intelligent control of planning would have made possible.

[1] *The Tenure of Agricultural Land*, Orwin and Peel, Cambridge University Press, 1926, p. 52.
[2] Cmd. 4605, 1934.

In this connection I cannot refrain from quoting the conclusion of Sir Daniel Hall's address to the British Association
at Nottingham on September 7th, 1937. He said:—

"It is easy to envisage the planning of the land of
Great Britain to ensure an increase in its productivity
and population if it could be treated as a great estate
managed by a business corporation with ample capital
to enable it to take a long view about development. Such
a plan can only be attained under the national ownership of the land. A plan is necessary not only in the
broad national interests of production, but also to prevent
the short-sighted destruction of the most valuable agricultural land and of the amenities of the countryside which
is everywhere going on to satisfy immediate urban requirements. British land is too limited and too precious to be
left to the unrestricted play of commercial exploitation."

Basis of Value

It is not realised as well as it ought to be that our existing
Land Valuation Department has branches in all parts
of the country and that every piece of agricultural land is
regularly valued. The valuation is based on the rent
received by the landlord after deductions have been made
for repairs and maintenance, for tithe, drainage rates and
other fixed outgoings. The amount thus arrived at is the
"net annual value" and appears regularly in the income
tax claims on owners of land as the assessment under
Schedule A. In the officially published programme of
the Labour Party this basis of value is accepted as the one
on which the purchase price would be estimated allowing
for its multiplication by a given number of years.

The case of the owner-occupier and the consideration of
allowances for timber plantations and other special values
will be taken later. We will take first the case of the
ordinary landlord owner who holds two-thirds or more of
the land. If 20 years' purchase on the basis of Schedule A
assessment were taken, and the assessment of a farmhouse

building and land was, say, £200 a year, the purchase consideration would be 200 × 20 = £4,000. Orwin and Peel allow 22½ years' purchase, but if we have regard to the findings of valuation tribunals—as, for example, in the recent valuation of mining royalties—it is most likely that a period somewhat less than 20 years would be reckoned as fair in the bulk of cases. There would, however, be no difficulty in setting up competent valuation tribunals to which appeal might be made where special consideration is claimed.

In fixing the number of years, however, the tribunal would take account of the reasonableness of the rents charged and the likelihood of their continuance, as well as the extent to which the landlord had fulfilled his responsibilities in regard to capital equipment, buildings, drainage, etc.

At my invitation, Mr. Ernest Davies has written a special critical examination of Compensation, and it is printed in Appendix III.—I recommend its careful perusal.

Mr. Davies suggests that the existing Acquisition of Land Act might provide that if the owner was not satisfied with a valuation based on Schedule A he might ask the tribunal to assess the value on the basis of the price at which "a seller could reasonably be expected to be willing to dispose of his land". For my part as one who was largely responsible for the Acquisition of Land Act of 1919, I think it is not too much to say that the basis therein provided has been found to work fairly and smoothly, and I see no objection to its being provided as an alternative if the owner wishes to make use of it instead of the Schedule A assessment basis. It is provided in the Acquisition of Land Act that the value is to "be taken to be the amount which the land, if sold in the open market, by a willing seller, might be expected to realise". The amount of land which has already been acquired for public purposes in this way is so great and the experience of the valuation officers is so widely esteemed and trusted, that agreement has frequently been arrived at without difficulty.

It should, however, be provided that, in fixing the amount of compensation, *no* allowance should be made for

1. Acquisition being compulsory or for any increased value that might result from its transfer to the State.
2. Existing or prospective site values where no expense or *bon-fide* liability had been incurred on that account before an appointed date.
3. Any undeveloped mineral rights.

Payment

Payment would be made by the issue to the present owner of Land Bonds to the amount of the purchase price determined. These Bonds would have behind them the security of the rents received from the land acquired as well as the land itself. The Bonds would be State Guaranteed Securities. For these reasons the National Commission would attach to them as low a rate of interest as that payable on the best Government Security. They would be saleable by their owner in the market like other securities and would be redeemable over a stated period.

Owner-Occupiers

Now turn to the much more difficult case of payment for land that is owned by its occupier.

The owner-occupier in a large number of cases has made great sacrifices to keep his home and farm together and should be encouraged and helped as much as possible. Short of any special necessity for amalgamation of land or other State requirements—for which compensation for disturbance would be payable—he should be given life security of tenure subject to a proper standard of cultivation, and the term might fairly cover the life of his widow or apply to his son, if continuing the farm as its occupier, for a given term of years after death. The land would, however, be vested in the Corporation and alienation would not be possible.

Many of those who bought their farms years ago will be found to be burdened with mortgages at a high rate of interest and in some cases the mortgages exceed the present value of the land. In no case, however, should

more compensation be paid than the land is worth, but
the mortgagee would receive Land Bonds to the full value
of the land where the amount of the mortgage was as great
as the value of the land. The farmer would pay rent to
the Corporation to the amount of the interest and redemption charges payable on the Bonds, and he would benefit
by the amount that the rate of interest on the Bonds was
less than the rate that he had previously paid on his
mortgage—probably from $1\frac{1}{2}$ to 2 per cent in the majority
of cases. We may be certain that such owner-occupiers
would welcome the scheme once they came to understand
its implication. They would find themselves provided with
a landlord able and willing to spend money on much-
needed improvements which they themselves had been
unable to afford.

In other cases the owner-occupier would be given
Bonds to the value of his holding and the interest payable
on them would be returned to the Corporation as rent so
far as the rent fixed might require. It will be seen that
in his appendix Mr. Davies makes additional suggestions
with regard to the basis of compensation for owner-
occupiers which differ from the Schedule A basis and
from the alternative of an appeal to the tribunal for a
market-value basis under the Acquisition of Land Act
that I have already suggested. I should be indisposed to
rule out any basis that may be considered fair, but as much
uniformity as possible is most desirable, and I believe that
the proposals already made will be found equitable.

Mr. Davies suggests that in view of the fact that the
owner-occupier pays no rent to himself he might be given
the option to ask for assessment of value on the basis of his
profits (Schedule D) over a term of years. On this, one may
say that comparatively few farmers keep their accounts in
such a form that correct ascertainment and disclosure of
profits are regularly made. Where this has been done it
will be mostly with the best farmers and one could not
fairly object to their claiming this alternative, although any
tribunal in assessing value would have regard to such facts

if put before them. In any case, however, they would have to be satisfied that there had been good husbandry.

Mr. Davies makes a further suggestion in his Scheme C that a rent-free basis during life and for an heir for a limited time thereafter, might be offered to owner-occupiers. It might be attractive where the expectation of life of the present owner-occupier and the subsequent period allowed exceeded the period of the redemption of the Bonds. It would involve no extra charge on the Land Fund, and I can see no reason why an owner-occupier might not have this option open to him on the lines suggested provided it did not stand in the way of necessary development and was accompanied by safeguards against alienation.

Beyond these two classes—the ordinary landlord owner and the owner-occupier—there would be a number of special cases that would claim consideration.

Special Cases

The most contentious would be those where a claim is made for Prospective Building Values.

Orwin and Peel seek to minimise the number of these cases by excluding from acquisition all land in cities, county boroughs, municipal boroughs and urban districts. During the last ten years, however, with the readjustments of boundaries, there have been many wide extensions of the limits of urban districts as well as of the larger municipalities and if the whole of the land, which is now in fact *bona fide* agricultural but is included in these enlarged boundaries, were excluded, one of the most important collateral advantages of the scheme would be lost. We are all familiar with the outcry that is continually being raised about ribbon development on improved or new roads. Many of these are included within the enlarged urban districts, and the biggest obstacle to the authorities in obtaining sufficient control over this form of development is the compensation they may be called upon to pay under the existing Act. There are manifest advantages in including all such lands that are at present agricultural. It would give ready and efficient control of planning and would moreover provide the State with a substantial future increment of value. There is no reason that I can see, either in justice or common sense, why such land should be excluded.

What is required is, that we should frame a scheme that is just. Where commitments have already been entered into, the assessment of compensation would present no difficulties, but it would be impossible to assess future values that are conjectural. The fair thing, therefore, appears to be that, where a claim to special consideration is established before the tribunal by a person prepared to undertake the expense of development, the land would pass to the State at the present agricultural valuation and the owner be given an option for a limited term of years to develop the land, or a part thereof, *in accordance* with plans approved by the Commission. He would then receive compensation to the extent of the additional values so established at the end of the agreed term. Compensation would, however, not be paid for anything other than the actual erection of houses or buildings or other necessary work connected with them, and in no case should the term allowed exceed, say, ten years.

The number of *Leaseholds* on ordinary agricultural land is small, but, where they do exist, all that would be necessary would be to divide the value between the ground landlord and the leaseholder, the former receiving that which would represent the present value of his reversion and the leaseholder the remainder.

Some private landowners have made *Timber Plantations* and they would be entitled to payment for the value so created that would be additional to the Schedule A basis. If the plantations were young and of a good type the payment should cover the cost of trees and planting with reasonable maintenance and interest allowance. If the timber was older and nearer a marketable age it would be in accordance with present practice of valuing growing timber to provide a sum that would represent the present value of the estimated worth of the timber at maturity.

The case of land that is already *Publicly owned* or owned by semi-public bodies, would also call for special treatment. Land attaching to asylums, water-works, sewage farms, railways, canals, burial grounds and such-like might be excluded. But the land belonging to National Bodies of the character of the Forestry Commission, War Departments, Colleges, Crown Lands, the Duchies of Cornwall and Lancaster, to the Departments of Agriculture as well as that acquired by Local Authorities for Small-holdings and Allotment purposes, should certainly be included in the general transfer to the Central State Authority. We may expect that there would be the usual departmental battles behind the scenes, but they would be capable of sensible adjustment. I have set out in Appendix IV a list of such lands publicly held, so far as I have been able to obtain details, and it will be seen that they represent in all a little more than three million acres. Some of it, such as College and Ecclesiastical lands, as well as some belonging to the Duchies, would fall within present town or city boundaries and be excluded, but the great bulk of the land is agricultural and should be included.

Finally, in connection with acquisition, the Times and Methods of *Transfer to the State* would be very important, both as regards the legitimate interest of present owners as well as of successful administration. It would be necessary in the Principal Act to provide that transfers should be made on "appointed days" and that due notice should be given beforehand of such appointments. Transfers would be made in terms of prescribed districts and not piecemeal. The process of valuation and transfer would necessarily take time, both in themselves and in the creation of the necessary administrative machinery, but we may anticipate, I think, that the total time required for transfer of title and management to the National Commission would not exceed five years. In any case the basis of valuation for all land would relate to the value on a date specified in the Principal Act and subsequent artificial inflation of values provided against.

PART II

SECTION III

Chapter IX

Finance, Management and Development

Financial Duties of the National Commission—Compensation and Development Bonds—Short-term Credit. *Administration* and County Committees—Duties—A Soil Survey—Promotion of Farming Enterprises—Large-scale, Specialist and Small-scale Farms—Equipment of Farms—Restoration of Neglected Land—Afforestation, Planning and Amenities.
Management—County Committees—Estate and Specialist Staffs—Their Duties.
The Future of Tithe.

W<small>E</small> <small>SHOULD NOW</small> consider the appropriate form of the National Machinery that would be required for the management of the business of land acquisition as well as for the development and equipment of land for improved use, including such measures of planning as may be required.

The National Agricultural Commission under the Minister of Agriculture is clearly the appropriate Body to have responsibility in major matters of policy and direction, with a special Land Department in executive charge.

A corresponding Authority would be required for Scotland under the Secretary of State, but with regard to matters affecting price and marketing, it would be necessary to provide for joint working of the two authorities.

It will be convenient to mention first the Financial Duties of the National Commission, then to discuss the form of the Local or District Agencies that would be required to secure practical and appropriate working, and afterwards to review the Developmental duties of the Commission and its local agents.

Finance

The National Commission would be responsible for three sets of financial operations: (1) Land Purchase;

(2) Development and Equipment; and (3) The Provision of Short-term Credit to Tenants.

In connection with Purchase, the National Commission would be responsible for the issue of the appropriate Bonds to the former owners. They may conveniently be described as Compensation Bonds.

Other Bonds would be issued from time to time to finance equipment, and may conveniently be described as Development Bonds. Both sets of Bonds would be a direct charge upon a Central Land Fund so far as interest and sinking fund charges were concerned, but the period of redemption of Compensation Bonds would necessarily be shorter than that attaching to those raised for Development purposes. The Commission, with its splendid national security, would be able to raise money at a low rate of interest and the lower the rate of interest the greater the advantage to agriculture with regard both to the rents required and to financing Development.

In the course of a few years increments of land value would begin to accrue to the Commission and its ability to undertake the redemption of Development Bonds would increase accordingly, but we have to recognise that expenditure under this head ought to be large in the early years because of the urgent need of the land for improved equipment and for capital provision in many forms. On account of this early demand for large expenditure Orwin and Peel suggest that the redemption of Development Loans should not begin until ten years after the initiation of the scheme. Against this, however, we have to remember that loans for these purposes would not be raised until the money was required and until the plans for development had been adequately prepared. Also the biggest items of expenditure would be in connection with the provision of buildings for which a long-term Sinking Fund period would be appropriate. For these reasons it would not, I think, be necessary to defer the commencement of Sinking Fund Payments on development account, especially as it is quite certain that, with rational guidance and a planned stimulation of development, the fund would rapidly become possessed of increased revenues from building and other eases.

In this connection we ought to make sure that sensible and progressive development would not be starved by the diversion of profits from the Land Account to the Treasury. If we were to allow the present example of Post Office profits to be imitated from the beginning it would paralyse development and involve the maintenance of a higher rental level than ought properly to be called for. I suggest in any case that no diversion of profits from the Land Account to the Treasury should take place until the full period of redemption of the Compensation Bonds had expired.

A very important service, as the scheme developed, would be the assistance of tenants by the Commission in the provision of Short-term Credit. The provision of such credit would necessarily be associated with the stabilised price arrangements and organised marketing schemes that would be developed, but there is no doubt that the provision of such credit for producers on an equitable and readily accessible basis, would be a very great service. One cannot say how much Producers are financed at present by merchants and others apart from the Banks, but there is much evidence of the extent to which Producers are crippled by the lack of an accessible system of short-term credit. The amount of use which has been made of the Agricultural Credits Act of 1928 and other Acts for improvements, apart from ordinary mortgages, is really trifling. The Lands Improvement Company up to the end of 1936 had made advances to Landowners of £1,584,873. The loans for Improvements made by the Agricultural Mortgage Corporation up to March 31st, 1936, amounted only to the trifling sum of £67,028 and a few small sums have been advanced by County Councils to Smallholders. When we consider this total of advances and compare it with the value of the nine million acres of land which belongs to owner-occupiers, apart from the estimated value of £280 million for tenants' capital as mentioned in the last chapter, we see how really insignificant it is. At the present time farmers are too tied up with mortgages, overdrafts at the Bank, debts to corn and cake merchants and others, to be in a position to make any effective use of this Act. We can, however, see great possibilities in this direction once the producer becomes able to sell his produce and buy his chief supplies, through an organisation that operates on his behalf and which would be an intrinsic part of the machinery of help that ought to be provided.

Administration

It will be convenient to defer consideration of the precise Constitution of the National Agricultural Commission and of its relation to the Ministry of Agriculture until we have taken account of its duties in connection with prices, marketing, and allied subjects; but it would require to be a National Authority of a highly competent character and staffed with the best men that can be obtained. It must also be under Government direction, since the Government of the country must be supreme.

These considerations, however, make it the more, not less, important that the Commission should be served by Local Agencies that would be in living, daily touch with the problems of cultivation and land management.

The duties that would require to be discharged locally would be of a twofold character. They would be concerned with Estate Management and with what may be described as Land Development and Farming Policy. This Local or District Agency must be in close and sympathetic touch with the needs of the cultivators as well as cognisant of the general plans of the Commission. It should evoke the goodwill and continued co-operation of those who are employed in the business of agriculture and this consideration must dictate to a large extent the form it should take.

Tradition and practice suggest that it would be most convenient to proceed on a County basis although in some

of the larger counties, and for special purposes, it may
be that a further sub-division might be found advantageous.
A County Committee, therefore, of appropriate constitution would appear to be the most convenient. The
form of the war-time Agricultural Committees consisting
of appointed persons naturally suggests itself, but sound
policy should aim, as I have said, at the continued and
friendly co-operation of those engaged in agriculture.
For this reason representatives suggested by the responsible
organisations of farmers and farm workers respectively
should form a large part of each County Committee. The
remainder would consist of persons experienced in Estate
Management and in the various Technical sides of the
industry as well as of other persons of special suitability.
The aim and object of the whole scheme is not only to get a
better planning of agriculture and an up-to-date equipment
of the land, but to put cultivators in a better position to do
their work and to bring to the service of the industry all the
aid that science and improved organisation can provide.

It will be better to consider the types of officers that
would require to be at the disposal of the Commission
and of the County Committee after we have looked at
some of the chief duties that would devolve upon these
Bodies. We must, however, be prepared to face up to those
critics whose standing objection to any National undertaking is that the country would be over-run by "hordes
of officials". As a matter of fact any well-managed system
will enormously reduce the multitude of those who batten
at present upon the unfortunate farmer in one form or
another. The scheme we are considering indeed will
involve immense economies in management as well as a
vast diminution in the number of those who now extract
their living from the industry in commissions of an infinite
variety. Criticisms about "hordes of officials" will, however, be prompt and plentiful and will have to be met
courageously. The scheme will ultimately be justified by
its success in leading to a fuller use of the land and in giving
a better life to the cultivator.

Duties—A Soil Survey

One of the first duties of the Commission and of the County Committees, so far as the land itself is concerned, would be co-operation in carrying out a much-needed Soil Survey. A sort of Doomsday Book of the Soil with a guide to its character and its suitability for different crops is badly wanted. For a long time past leading agricultural authorities have stressed the need of such a survey and of its results being made available on suitable maps of the different districts. With the staffs employed by the Ministry of Agriculture and the County Councils and the different Agricultural Colleges the work need not occupy a long period or be very expensive. In an interesting article on the subject Mr. S. L. Bensusan[1] gave some striking figures as to the mosaic of soils that is to be found in Great Britain. He says, for example, that in the Hastings Beds in Kent there are sixteen different soil series, and that in the Lower Greensand in Kent there are twenty-six. He relates an incident, of which many of us have experienced parallel cases:—It is that of a man who proposed to purchase two hundred acres of land in a southern county for fruit growing—particularly for dessert apples—but, before committing himself, he was wise enough to obtain an expert examination of the soil. The result showed that there were only about ten acres fully suitable for his purpose, although the land was good for some other purposes. If we are to obtain the best and most suitable production from the land, and especially in such an emergency as that of war, a Soil Survey is essential. The fruits of it would be a standing guide to the planning of future development. It would contain information upon the character of the soil itself, upon its topography, natural drainage and kindred matters.

Farming Methods

Another early, but continuing duty of the Commission, with the advice and help of its County Committees and

[1] The *Spectator*, July 24th, 1936.

special officers, would be the planning of agricultural development with regard to national needs and policy in the light of soil capacity.

We may take it that for a long time to come tenant farming would be the predominant type and the measure of security that ought to be given to good cultivators would ensure the retention of it to a wide extent. The proved adaptability also of up-to-date farmers is an indication of the extent to which their co-operation in new ventures or methods might be obtained.

Nevertheless, by deaths, removals or other causes there are many changes every year, and there would be ample room for the development of other types of farming as experience develops. Amongst these, large-scale farming operations in appropriate districts would certainly be prominent. There is need also for the application both on rough grazings and on wold lands, as well as on some richer lands, of many of the new methods that are proving their value and which are only possible when plenty of capital, experienced management and good accounting are available.

In the Land Utilisation Act of 1931, as introduced, I incorporated proposals for the establishment of a Large-scale Farming Corporation with £1,000,000 capital. This proposal had to be dropped as the price of getting the Bill through the House of Lords and the decision to do so was justified because of what could be accomplished under the other provisions of the Act if they were applied. This procedure of large-scale farming will be examined in detail when we come to consider a Development Programme, but it is a profound mistake to suppose, as is commonly represented, that a great reduction in labour employment is necessarily involved. Examples will be given of large-scale farming operations which have been accompanied by increased labour employment. The possibilities of increased production are so great, for example in the case of live-stock, that they may lead to the employment of more labour on the same lands than before. Similarly it has been found that large-scale farming with high mechanisation applied to the production of market garden supplies has meant a large increase in the labour employed.

Another development that would certainly be undertaken in suitable districts would be the extension of Specialised Farming of different types. These specialised farms would vary from those conducted on a large scale to more intensive cultivation in a great variety of forms. As an example, I may say that I am authoritatively informed that the London market could absorb the produce of an additional twenty thousand acres devoted to the production of winter salads.

Specialised farming in different forms might form a part of some Land Settlement Schemes, although in my judgment the possibilities of development in this form have been much exaggerated. I shall, however, deal with this subject later on as a part of a Development Programme. For the present it suffices to point out that the promotion of Land Settlement, to whatever extent it might be found to be desirable, would be associated with the work of the National Commission. It would indeed be folly to rule out in advance any form of development of cultivation. We must have a plan that will make use in a progressive form of the lessons which science and increased knowledge may place at our disposal.

Equipment

Another duty for the Commission—and perhaps the most urgent of all in the early years of its work—would be that of dealing with the deplorable conditions of equipment into which much of our land has fallen. The Commission would be inundated with demands. The more enlightened and progressive its County Committees or advisers were, the greater would be the demand. The expenditure required for new or improved buildings, for water supplies, for drainage and for fertilisation purposes would be so great that it would require to be carefully planned and would call for a long-term programme

HA

of development. A National Water-Supply Organisation
should be created anyhow; and the demands of the
Agricultural Commission would certainly hasten the
formation of such a Body if it had not previously been
created. In any case we should become emancipated
from the silly attempt to deal with the water-supply
needs of extensive districts in terms of separate parish
schemes and should be able to reap the economies and
better services that would be derived from plans based
on the best engineering advice obtainable, and be able
to proceed without being handicapped all the time by
claims for compensation as the pipes passed from the
patch of one owner to that of another.

There is indeed so much to be done, so great a neglect
of buildings, drainage, water supplies, fencing and fertility
that the difficulty in the early years would be that of a
wise choice as to where to begin and in what order to
proceed. It certainly would not be long before the
advantages derived from the operations of the National
Commission in these directions would justify Professor
Stapledon's forecast[1] that "the occupiers would welcome
the State as their landlord in return for the facilities and
general prosperity that would follow in the wake of
rejuvenation all round", although the rate of progress
might not satisfy Mr. Street's farmer friend, already quoted,
who exclaimed:[2] "I don't care a damn what it costs to effect
this, I am sure the outlay will repay the nation tenfold."

Another part of the re-equipment duties of the Commission would relate to the large amount of useful land
that has practically passed out of farming through neglect,
and is now classed as land in need of "restoration". The
scandalous cases like that of the derelict farms already
referred to in Chapter V would be the grosser cases only.
At the time of the Land Utilisation Act the area of land
in need of restoration and likely to justify work upon it
was roughly estimated at five million acres. Whatever

[1] *Hill Lands of Britain*, Faber & Faber, 1937, p. 100.
[2] A. G. Street, *Farming England*, p. 8.

it is, however, it would provide a great and splendid task. At the same time the Commission would become responsible for promoting the better use of the hill-lands Professor Stapledon has so forcibly written about, as well as the restoration to food production of some of the land that has been absorbed for the purposes of Sport. At long last, also, thank God, we should also be in sight of the redemption of some of the disgraces of the Scottish Highland evictions.

Afforestation

In the previous chapter it was suggested that the land now belonging to the Forestry Commission should be incorporated in the National Lands that would be brought under the authority of the proposed Commission. The Forestry Commission should become a special department under the Commission. This will be a contentious subject. I have a lively recollection of the acrimonious discussions that went on behind the scenes in 1918 over the establishment of the present Forestry Commission when it was my duty as Minister of Reconstruction to hold the balance as fairly as I could. I have no doubt that, whether in public or not, we should have a return of this controversy when it was proposed to make the control of Forestry policy one of the functions of the Agricultural Commission. But it ought to be done. At the present time, owing to the difficulty of acquiring land that ought properly to be afforested in a progressive programme, the Commission is continually obliged to take up land that is not the most suitable and often in odd and inadequate patches. Only under National ownership, and with the consideration of plans alongside the proper examination of other possible uses of the Land, as well as the relation thereto of the claims of beauty and amenities, can a satisfactory forestry policy be made possible.

Planning and Amenities

In conclusion, there would be a set of duties for the National Commission that should bring joy to the heart of every lover of our countryside. Afforestation if properly planned on land appropriate for the purpose, need not spoil the attractiveness and harmony of rural England. It might indeed enhance it. So far as building developments are concerned there is abundant justification for what Mr. Clough Williams Ellis has said in his *Britain and the Beast*. Ribbon development and spoliation in a hundred forms are proceeding apace. Planning is entangled in a hopeless network of claims, hearings and arbitrations. One district is not prepared to pay at all; another is confronted with claims for compensation of such a character that it cannot possibly face up to it; and so on, and so on. We are presented with a bewildering and disgusting paralysis of the restraint of spoliation. In an article entitled "British and Beastly" in the *London Mercury* of August 1937, Mr. Williams Ellis summed up his impressions of the suggestions for control that had emerged from the criticisms evoked by his book. He found that they were so confused that he rendered the signal service of formulating suggestions of his own. He wants a "Ministry of Planning and Design". He urges that private ownership of undeveloped urban land should be rationalised or abolished. He urges that the Ministry of Planning and Design should develop a National Park Policy, and that it should be vigorously pursued. He wants a "Certificate of Seemliness" for proposed buildings, the control of landscape advertising, the amendment of the Town and Country Planning Act and other reforms. When we come to examine these proposals and try to find out how they would work we are forced to recognise that the difficulty at the heart of things is that we have no National Body with control of the Land itself. Anyone who takes the trouble to acquaint himself with the claims for compensation that may arise under the Ribbon Development Act, as well as with the complicated machinery of the Town and Country Planning Act, must be convinced that our efforts will continue to be futile until we can obtain control of the land.

Under the National scheme that we are here considering, a National Authority with appropriate powers could readily be brought into being. It would not only be required to be the vigilant custodian of the maintenance of landscape beauty, but it would be required to provide and control footpaths as well as access to mountains and beautiful places under sensible conditions. It would also promote the provision of lodging and other facilities for trampers and countryside visitors, as well as scheduling specified areas that should be specially preserved.

The subject is closely allied to Forestry work in many districts and will be returned to in a later chapter when the Development of Forestry work is proposed.

District Management

In the light of this review of the duties of the National Agricultural Authority, let us return to the question of Management.

The management must, as already said, be the business of those who are on the spot and who have daily contact with its needs.

Management in this case would be of two types—Estate Management, including specialist officers, and the management of Farming Development.

Estate Management calls for special knowledge and experience. There are many properties up and down the country which are suffering at present because their owners are not in a position to employ the necessary expert assistance. One of the first advantages that would arise out of National ownership in this respect would be the possibility of a sensible grouping of farm lands in sufficiently large units for proper estate management. At the same time there would be a need for the services of experts in different branches of the industry.

There would therefore be two types of staff; Estate staffs and Specialist staffs. With regard to the latter most County Councils at the present time have an Agricultural Organiser who is responsible for the supervision and management of the County Smallholdings as well as for giving advisory services to farmers. Under the Agricultural Organiser, in most counties there are experts in stock raising, horticulture, and poultry work. These men have gained the confidence and respect of the farmers and are often very overworked by the demands that are made upon them. Services of this kind will grow in importance and should provide the basis of a first-class public service.

There would be little difficulty in obtaining the necessary assistance in Estate Management. There are capable men at present employed on the different estates who would be taken into a national system, as well as many others who now work on their own account. The work of estate management would include negotiations for the letting of farms, the supervision of estates, reports on the needs for equipment, drainage, etc., the preparation of plans, the carrying out of surveys and many kindred technical matters. The same groups of officers, together with the technical experts, would have to make reports on the desirability of the amalgamation of farms, on the needs that were associated with proposals for land settlement or specialised farming, apart from the day-to-day questions which the experts would be called upon to answer in connection with the marketing proposals that will be described later on.

These staffs would be grouped according to the areas dealt with by the County Committees already referred to. In some of the larger counties there would be a sub-division into districts, whilst in the smaller counties a joint working might be arranged for.

Some County Councils, such as Lancashire and Norfolk, have considerable staffs employed in connection with their large smallholding undertakings, and joint working arrangements between the National Commission and the County Council would no doubt be arranged for in such cases. Nevertheless both the Estate and Specialist officers should be regarded as servants of the National Commission, and form part of a National Service that will provide its own opportunities for advancement. They would be attached, in their different areas, to the County Committees that would be set up to assist the National Commission.

Farming Development involves a national effort to restore agriculture; and, for reasons already explained, one cannot imagine its being successfully prosecuted unless the co-operation of those engaged in the industry—farmers and farm workers alike—is enlisted. The suggestions already made for the Constitution of County Committees embody the proposals set out by the Labour Party and I cannot but think that they are on the right lines. They would require before long that every farmer would be a member of his Union and every Agricultural worker of his. This is as it ought to be. We shall then begin to get a pooling of experience in the interests of the industry itself such as we have never yet been able to evoke.

The aim should be to fashion an agency that will bring to the aid of the scheme the goodwill and experience of those who are engaged in it for the purpose of improving the industry itself.

The County Committees would be the local agents of the National Commission, served by the Estate and Specialist officers already referred to. They would be concerned with the provision and maintenance of a proper standard of equipment, advice upon the letting of farms, the consideration of proposals for farm amalgamation, for the establishment of demonstration farms, for the provision of better facilities for training and education, for making more freely available the benefits of improved knowledge and for the maintenance of a good standard of husbandry and other matters.

I should be reluctant to endow these Committees with some of the more drastic powers that were possessed by the County Executive Committees of the war period. In the majority of cases, no doubt, the Commission would seek the advice of the County Committees when the reports of the Estate or other officers led to the suggestion that drastic action required to be taken for neglect or bad farming, but there are many advantages for the final decision in such cases being attached to the National Commission.

After we have examined the subject of prices and organised marketing we shall see that there are other duties that will attach to County Committees.

Before passing to those important agricultural subjects, however, I ought to add a note on what would appear to be the right course to take on the subject of Tithe charges on land.

Tithe

The Tithe Act of 1936 and the establishment of the present Tithe Commission removed many of the old standing causes of controversy between farmers and the Church, although tithe payments continue. In effect the Government has assumed responsibility; and the prolongation of the Sinking Fund period has diminished to some extent the amount of the annual payments by tithe payers.

The gross inequalities of the distribution of tithe amongst benefices remain, but they are ecclesiastical rather than agricultural issues. In any case it is safe to predict that whenever agricultural land is transferred to State ownership we shall find the existing arrangements in being, although we may hope that the change will have been effected long before the Sinking Fund period has ended.

Although the payment of a tithe charge diminishes the rental value of the land affected it is quite unthinkable that these accidental charges on particular holdings should continue under a National system. When the time came we should have to make the best of things as they were and the right course to pursue would be to pool the tithe payments that are made on agricultural land and make the amount payable out of the Central Land Fund. Those who would be the occupiers of holdings previously paying tithe, would be relieved of these payments and have their holdings assessed instead on a fair-rent basis.

PART II

SECTION IV

Chapter X

Essentials of Price Management

Success Essential—The Failure of other Devices: Tariffs, Quotas, Quantitative Regulation, Subsidies—Control of Supply Essential: Home-produced and Imported.
Distribution—The Causes of High Retail Prices—Local Distributors' Associations—The Multiplicity of Shops—The "Convenience" of Customers.

THE TRANSFER OF all the farmland of the country to National possession is a big undertaking, no doubt; but it would not require any procedures of which we are without previous experience, nor would it be difficult in itself. But when we seek to give effect to the purposes for which the land has been obtained we are confronted by many new and difficult undertakings. We shall be seeking to use the land for the first time with the deliberate purpose of ministering to the food needs of the people and at the same time of ensuring that it will be used under such conditions that a good cultivator will obtain a decent living and be emancipated from the perils and uncertainties of a system under which, however well he may conduct his business, he may still find that he is working at a loss.

Nevertheless the turmoil and expense of transferring all the land from private to public ownership will have been in vain unless this can be accomplished. It must be accomplished if we are to make our country what it ought to be.

So far as the Producer himself is concerned, whatever system of society we live under in which money is used as an instrument of exchange, his ability to pay the standard of wages society will require and to provide for himself and his family will depend upon how much he receives for his produce as compared with what it costs him to produce it.

The day has passed when we can be deterred by those who would tell us "you can't interfere with the law of supply and demand", whatever that "law" may be. As my friend Sir A. W. Street contended in a brilliant address at Cambridge to County Agricultural Organisers, in June 1935, when discussing the need for a close relation between Agricultural policy and National needs. We cannot accept the alternation of slumps and booms of the past, with prosperity of the producer one day, and ruin the next, as if they were the result of some economic law or other that we must submit to with such resignation as we can command. We see around us the discreditable contrast of over-abundance and semi-starvation, of over-work and unemployment, and Society will not, for ever, tolerate that these things shall endure. They must be corrected somehow. They cannot be corrected save by comprehensive planning and effective organisation. Indeed, as Street concluded, "we must seek to secure control of our economic and social destiny before it is too late".

How are we to do it so far as the Home Producers and Consumers of Food are concerned?

The first thing that leaps to our eyes is that we cannot do it unless we are prepared to make fundamental alterations in the present system of food marketing. We must get rid of the pernicious influence of a system which handles supplies for the purpose of making as much profit out of them as possible without regard to the interests of the producer and the consumer.

It cannot be contended nowadays that it is impossible to manage prices so as to introduce stability into them. The real questions are: Who is to do the managing? And for what purpose? Is it to be done by powerful corporations for the purpose of making as much profit as possible, or is it to be done on behalf of the community with the general well-being as the end in view? The pace towards the former method has been very rapid during the past twenty years, and the longer society shirks its duty in undertaking its responsibilities, the more difficult they will become.

Free competition never was a safeguard for the people. The records of the industrial revolution prove that in the wretched condition of employment and housing it created and which we are still struggling to redeem. So far also as free competition is still left, it is being whittled away more and more every year. The present-day apostles of it are living in a past world.

The Steel Corporation dictates the price of steel. The Petrol Companies decide how much we are to pay for petrol. The Light Castings Association could put out of business any ironmonger who refused to sell their goods on the prescribed condition, and the Proprietary Articles Trades Association could do the same for anyone who sells the numerous goods the Association controls if he failed to "play the game". Perhaps one of the most striking examples of the disastrous power of Trade Associations that operate for the motive of Profit only is afforded in the records of the four great American Tobacco Companies. Between 1919 and 1931 these great united concerns increased their production by 120 per cent. The prices to the consumer were not reduced; but the payments to the growers were reduced from 30 cents per lb. to 8 cents. The number of workers was reduced by 18 per cent, and the total wage bills by 30 per cent.

What in all these cases, and in others like them, is the key to the power of these Combinations? It is that at some place or another, in their passage from the producer to the consumer, *they are in control of the Supplies*. They do not need to be the actual producers; all they need is to be in control of some stage or process, some "bottle-neck" or other, through which the supplies pass.

If we are to see our fellow citizens get enough to eat and are not exploited in what they have to pay for it, and at the same time secure for those at home who provide an important share of that food the conditions they are entitled to, then we must institute in appropriate forms the necessary control over the supplies of that food. Such control must be comprehensive if it is to be efficient; and it must sufficiently safeguard the conditions of sale, transport,

preservation and distribution. If these can be obtained, then
we shall be able to plan the best utilisation of the land and
to make a full and eager use of all the powers which science
and increasing knowledge place at our disposal.

Before analysing what such powers will involve, it will be
useful to look at the various devices that have been employed during the past five years by the present Government
to provide a price system that will satisfy the home producer.
The fact that these devices have failed so far to do what has
been aimed at is evidenced by the existing discontent as
well as by the constant attempts to apply new expedients.

Tariffs

So far as food is concerned Tariffs have only been
employed to a limited extent. In some measure they have
been employed side by side with "Quotas" or with some
form of Quantitative Regulation, so that we cannot with
confidence disentangle the effects of the tariff from that
of the rest. The outstanding fact about tariffs, so far as
food supplies are concerned, is that they cannot possibly
be applied in an extreme form because of our large dependence upon imported supplies.

A Duty upon an imported supply necessarily tends to
increase its price on the market, but it does not guarantee
the provision of abundant supplies for the people; it
does not promote economies in the process of distribution
nor does it do anything to improve the conditions of the
supply of home-produced goods coupled with stable prices
for the producer. In addition to this, a tariff does not
furnish any incentive to improve efficiency in the production of the home product, nor to an enhanced consideration
of the wants of the consumer. It may, in fact, support
inefficiency in so far as it may raise the general level of
price without calling for any improvement in production
methods. Neither do tariffs help to prevent the recurrent
slumps to which agriculture, in common with other
industries, is exposed under the present system. At the
same time they do not rule out the possibility of dumping

or forced selling, especially where the British market is the chief market. Their intended effect also is sometimes neutralised by export bounties in one form or another. A good example of this is afforded in the record of what happened after the 40 per cent *ad valorem* duty was imposed on fat cattle from Ireland. The Irish Government promptly provided an export bounty: and the result was that more fat cattle came from Ireland during the twelve months following the first imposition of the duty than had been supplied in the previous twelve months. I am not in the least concerned here to discuss the rights or wrongs of tariffs generally, but it is surprising that so many farmers still cling to them as a panacea for their ills in view of the obvious limitations that must attach to their use in a country like ours which is so dependent upon outside food supplies.

If we exclude wheat (which is now dealt with by a different method) the chief food imports, similar to those produced at home, are beef, mutton, pig-meat, butter, cheese, eggs, potatoes, and some kinds of fruit. It is unthinkable that any Government would put such a tax on any of these food supplies as would raise their price to the level that is really in the minds of those who advocate them.

Quotas and Quantitative Regulation

The Quota system—by which is meant the allocation to another country of a given quantity of produce for importation—is in fact only a part of what is aimed at under the more comprehensive system commonly described as "Quantitative Regulation". So far as Quantitative Regulation means a system of the orderly and sufficient supply of the requirements of the market, it is clearly an essential part of an organised and properly managed system. As such it is essential to a rational planning of the relation between home production and imported supplies. But unless it is accompanied by the other powers and arrangements necessary for its proper and successful use in ministering to the needs of the people for food, it may become discredited. Indeed it is in serious danger of being so at the present time.

We have repeatedly been told by Government spokesmen that its "purpose" is not to raise prices but to substitute for unregulated importation a system of orderly supply. Whatever its professed purpose, however, it has undoubtedly been used so far only for supporting or increasing prices except that to some extent it has been of use in substituting a method of peaceful conference with foreign suppliers for the ill-feeling which tariffs or the irregular application of quotas might have engendered. It can, in fact, only have the effect of bolstering up prices, whether intentional or not, so long as it is unaccompanied by the other arrangements for the sufficient control of the processes of distribution, as well as by the other powers over supply, that are necessary to provide a reliable price system in the home market. So long as Quantitative Regulation fails to be a part of a comprehensive plan framed for these purposes, it may be very dangerous. It tends to consolidate monopoly amongst exporters and to some extent amongst the importing agencies, and it presents a standing temptation for it to be used to raise prices by inducing artificial scarcity. Indeed, so far as it has been used at present we can justly say that that has been its effect.

For example, the first result of the operations of Quantitative Regulation in the case of beef was to put up the price of chilled beef from the Argentine. But it did not result in the producer of British beef getting a better price. What happened, in fact, was the opposite. The housewife looking for her weekly joint found that the price of beef had gone up. She did not therefore buy the higher-priced British beef (she had no more money in her pocket than the week before) so she looked for a cheaper joint or bought less beef. The result was a damaging effect upon the beef-eating habit and three months afterwards the price of British beef was lower than before. The best proof of its inadequacy in this case is the fact that the taxpayer is now being called upon to pay such immense subsidies for home-produced beef.

The result of applying Quantitative Regulation under present conditions to Danish bacon was even more striking. Directly after the first restriction was imposed the holders of bacon supplies put up the price. Every wholesaler and dealer, from the port to the retail counter, was uncertain as to what would be the effect and took the only course they could of safeguarding themselves—namely of adding a little to the price. The result was that within a few months the price of bacon over the counter had gone up so much that people bought less bacon. They went without their breakfast rasher. At the end of twelve months the consumer was paying $2\frac{1}{2}d.$ per lb. more for his bacon whilst the home producer was getting $1d.$ more.

Moreover, Quantitative Regulation alone, as the price changes showed, introduced no stability into the market. It gave no satisfaction to the shopkeeper or to the housewife, and very little to the British farmer. The proof, after four years, is manifest in the present chaotic position of the bacon industry. There is indeed a grave danger that, used in this way, as a sort of isolated piece of machinery, the whole process of the management of supply that is so necessary may be discredited.

Subsidies

The failure of this mixture of tariffs, quotas and quantitative regulation is now being sought to be atoned for by a system of subsidies. Reference has already been made to the case of Beef, but it is worth closer examination. It represents a courageous although exceedingly costly attempt to provide reliable prices for the home producer of beef by the method of subsidy without accepting the inevitable necessity of the proper management of the market. The subsidy was begun in September 1934 and its design was to add 5s. per cwt. to the price that cattle of the right quality made in the market. A competent Committee was appointed to manage the payments. The idea was to give the farmers 5s. more per cwt. than they were then obtaining, and to enable them to receive this increased price without adding to the cost in the butcher's shop. The result was that the price bid in the market fell nearly to the extent of the subsidy, and the accompanying table shows what happened for two years.

MEAN AVERAGE PRICES OF
1st AND 2nd QUALITY SHORTHORNS
(Subsidy Payments Commenced September 1934)

1934

3rd quarter.	7 weeks prior to subsidy	Subsidy begins.	4th quarter.
37/8	40/3		34/6

1935

1st quarter.	2nd quarter.	3rd quarter.	4th quarter.
33/8	34/8	33/8	33/3

1936

1st quarter.	2nd quarter.	3rd quarter.
34/10	36/9	36/1

Up to June 1937 Parliament had voted £10,500,000 for this subsidy and, if we are to take the prices prevailing at its commencement as the standard of price that the subsidy was to supplement, it means that, at most, the farmers have obtained about £4,000,000 of the money voted, whilst £6,500,000 have been completely absorbed by the other participators in the existing distribution system.

During 1937 the price of beef went up along with that of other commodities, but the undeniable fact that farmers have been receiving only a portion of what they expected, and of what Parliament provided for them, has led to widespread dissatisfaction. The result is seen in the other proposals on this subject made in the Cattle Industry Bill of 1937.

It is therein proposed to close some of the smaller open markets and to provide three large Abattoirs to receive cattle from prescribed areas. So far as these half-hearted proposals go they will introduce some measure of control into the market, and provide—in the selected districts at least—the machinery whereby the home producer will be honestly paid for what he sends. The significance of them is that the logic of the facts is compelling even a Conservative Government to nibble at the inevitable. These measures will not, of course, be described as "Socialistic". They will be spoken of as "Organisation". But what of that.

The point is that they give recognition to the fact that if we desire to secure a fair and reliable price for the producer we must introduce machinery to see that he gets it. In the case of cattle destined for slaughter, the obvious place for that machinery is the abattoir.

The extraordinary thing is that we should find ourselves still having to insist on the need for this abattoir system because it is one on which the Government of the country, for several years past, has been provided with emphatic advice. I myself was responsible, when Minister of Agriculture, for initiating the appointment of the Committee on the Slaughtering of Livestock that issued its report in 1933[1]. Anyone who cares to read it will find a condemnation in advance of the futility of the partial measures of the Livestock Bill of 1937.

The Report showed that, apart from other substantial gains, the farmers might receive an additional £2 3s. 4d. on each head of cattle sent for slaughter if they were all passed through an organised abattoir system. This £2 3s. 4d. is made up of three items: A saving on commissions and auctions charges of 15s. a head; a saving of 13s. 4d. by the avoidance of needless moving about of the cattle and depreciation of quality, and 15s. from sales of by-products. This figure also was arrived at after making full allowance for abattoir expenses. It is almost incredible that with facts like these staring them in the face we should still find the National Farmer's Union hoping for salvation from duties on Argentine Beef. We shall, however, gain some light upon the silence that has been applied to these revelations when we come to look closer at the interests supporting the present system of Distribution. At the moment, however, the point is that if we want to secure a dependable price system for the home producer of good beef it is through the abattoir that it will be obtained.

This case illustrates the fact that the method of management of the marketing of any commodity must vary with its character as well as with the nature of the channels

[1] Report to the Economic Advisory Council, 1933, pp. 63–79.

IA

that it passes through. The great American tobacco corporations previously referred to are not themselves the growers of the tobacco plants, but they provide, by their combination, the only channels through which the growers can sell their produce. The Light Castings Association is an association of Manufacturers that operates through an agreement to associate for price, and it secures thereby a stabilised price system for all concerned. The control of the Proprietary Articles Trades Association is exercised in a different way and covers manufactures of a great variety. In this case it controls the price conditions under which the retailer may sell. The essential fact, however, is that, by diverse arrangements operating at some place in the market channel, uniformity of quotation is secured for a multitude of articles as widely different as bedsteads and pills. It is therefore nothing short of silly to pretend that we cannot if we like, in the interests of the home producer and the consumer, devise appropriate arrangements for price management of beef or eggs or of any other major food supply.

The arrangements, however, to be efficient, must cover *all* of the supply of the given commodity, both home-produced and imported. In some cases, as already said, the commodities may be dealt with in groups, but the principles of management are the same in all cases.

The wise method to proceed in the development of a considered plan would be to begin with such major commodities as bacon, meat, milk, eggs and poultry, in which, from the nature of the case, it would be easier to achieve success. In other cases, such, for example, as market-garden produce, where existing practice and seasonality of supply present special difficulties, the right course would be to proceed by the working out of intermediate arrangements that are on the lines of future development.

In our next chapters we shall examine in detail the powers or uses of Home-Producers and of Import Boards, but before we conclude this preliminary review reference must be made to distribution.

Distribution

It is certain that in attempting to effect economies in distribution and to diminish the unwarrantable difference between the prices paid to the producer and by the consumer, we shall be confronted with great difficulties, but I do not think that, if the case is properly handled, it need result in serious conflict. In any case it is useless to pretend that we shall ever get an efficient food-supply and production system unless the case is dealt with successfully.

Many leaders of the Distributive industry—both in the Co-operative movement and in privately managed concerns—have frequently expressed their anxiety over the shocking discredits of the present system; but things seem to grow worse rather than better. The producer of cabbages that I spoke of in Chapter III is only one of many thousands, although perhaps it may be difficult to find many cases as extreme as his when the cabbages for which he was paid a quarter of a farthing each in the morning were sold the same afternoon for forty times as much retail; but cases like his are characteristic of local gluts. It is, however, quite common to find retail prices to be three or four times that of the producer. Even in the case of a commodity of everyday production and consumption, like Milk, where there is a powerful Producers' Board in existence, the price is nearly double.

It is no good blaming the distribution trade for these results. They are inseparable from the present system. "Free Competition" in distribution indeed seems to enhance the retail price rather than reduce it. The retail price of milk, for example, is in fact that prescribed by the distributors as a body in the different districts, and the purpose of it is to secure that each of them—even the least efficient distributor—will be able to carry on. We find, therefore, an extraordinary number of small distributors who sell only a few gallons each per day, but they carry on somehow by the support of these distributors agreements. The whole influence of this kind of thing keeps up retail prices instead of diminishing them.

How powerful it is, when it is represented in a national

form, is seen in the latest price agreement of the Milk Marketing Board. It is thus described in the October number (1937) of the *National Farmers' Union Record:*—

"The Milk Marketing Board has been placed under the sheer necessity of adopting the deplorable expedient of reaching a milk contract agreement for 1937–8 which involves retail price increases and gives the distributors an actual margin substantially in excess of their nominal margin of profit."

This agreement, it should be noticed, is one to which the Co-operative movement is a party as well as many other well-managed concerns who would gladly reduce prices if they were allowed. The pressure behind prevents them. It would be difficult to imagine a more significant example of the immense influence at present exercised to maintain high retail prices. In this case it has actually been preceded by the formal findings of more than one Government Commission, as well as of the Food Council, that retail milk prices *ought* to be reduced, *could* be reduced, and *must* be reduced, if the public are to obtain the milk that they need. Yet so powerful is the influence of an uneconomic Distribution system that the prices are actually increased.

A recent pamphlet written for the National Amalgamated Union of Shops Assistants, Warehousemen and Clerks, by Mr. P. C. Hoffman gives some figures of the Distributive Trade up to 1934. In 1921, 996,080 people found employment in distribution, but in 1934 the figure had increased to 2,142,000! At the previous date one person in every forty-three had been employed in distribution in one form or another, but at the latest date the total had increased to the extraordinary proportion of one person out of every sixteen of the whole population. In 1934 there were no less than a million shops of one kind or another in the United Kingdom —one for every forty-four persons of the population. This means, and can only mean, that thousands of struggling shopkeepers are trying to get a living by working every hour they are allowed to work and that sweated wages and bad working conditions in multitudes of small shops are inevitable.

This endeavour to get a living by keeping a little shop is one of the by-products of unemployment and has continued notwithstanding the immense progress that has been made by some of the larger concerns. It is no wonder, therefore, that in consequence of the pressure from local Distributors' Associations to maintain the retail price level, some of the large and well managed concerns, as Mr. Hoffman says, have distributed "luscious" dividends although some of them are probably much over-capitalised. If, however, we take the large concerns along with the Co-operative societies, they represent only 4 per cent of the total shops although they do 30 per cent of all the business.

These are some of the staggering facts we have to bear in mind. It is no good shouting about it or blaming shopkeepers. They are doing the best they can with the world as it is. The public also has a large share of responsibility for this state of affairs. Under the shelter of these retail price understandings there has arisen a real competition to meet what is described as the "convenience" of customers, and people come, more and more, to expect distribution services which must be costly. Often enough milk is delivered from door to door in half-pints twice daily, even in the winter time when the day's full quantity will keep perfectly well. The butcher is asked to send a couple of chops a mile or more, and the baker and grocer also have to maintain costly services in vans and labour which, often enough for many errands, must cost as much as the goods themselves. Here and there people get their milk at reduced prices if they send for it, but in the main all these "convenience" costs of distribution find their expression in a higher level of retail prices than need be the case. If, therefore, we are to achieve a reduction of distribution costs there must be a substantial measure of co-operation by the people themselves.

The case can only be met by promoting rational and economical arrangements, first in one commodity and then in another, and I will do my best in subsequent chapters to make suggestions as to how it should be approached.

PART II

SECTION V

Chapter XI

Producers' Boards

The Marketing Act of 1931 only the First Stage—Purposes of Producer's Boards—Powers and Duties—Illustrated by Reference to the Marketing of Eggs—Maintenance of Consumption—Reliability of Price—A National Price—Other Necessities—List of the Powers and Duties of Producers' Boards—Not Fitted to Deal with Distribution.

WHEN WE TRY to make use of the considerations discussed in the last chapter so as to guide us to the form of organisation that would be required for the home-producer, we are confronted with the difficulties that arise from the day-to-day realities of the industry. It was these realities that dictated the form of the Agricultural Marketing Act of 1931. It was designed to deal with the first stage only of the plan of reorganisation that was before us. That Act was to have been, and some day will have to be, followed by proposals for dealing with the allied and inseparable problems of Imported supplies, Distribution and Price Control. But we shall get a better view of what is required if we examine in the first place the essentials of a home-producer's organisation.

The production of any one of our chief food supplies is in the hands of many thousands of separate producers scattered up and down the country with established, and often conflicting, habits, traditions and prejudices. They constitute an intensely individualistic class of people, and there is no set of our fellow citizens with whom you are less likely to succeed if you proceed with the notion "that you can order them about". Nevertheless it is absolutely certain that you cannot provide for them the benefits of the reliable price system they all wish to have, whatever their personal inclinations, unless you can arrange somehow or another that there is a sufficient measure of control over the marketing of the commodity you are trying to deal with. That control also will not be effective unless it is comprehensive. How are you to get a comprehensive system with a multitude of separate producers like this?

It is a first necessity that you must try and frame a plan in which they will be willing to co-operate.

A Producers' Organisation of the right kind can render many valuable services apart entirely from price assistance. Some of them are badly needed by agriculturalists, and can only be rendered through, or by, a combined organisation. But if we are ever to get to a position in which we can reap the advantages obtainable by these means, we must, in the first instance, establish an organisation that will satisfy the producer that he will, at long last, be assured that he will get a fair price for his produce and be delivered from the hazards he suffers from at present.

The First Producers' Board that came into existence as a result of the Act of 1931 was the Hops Board; and the reasons for this were twofold. There had previously been in existence an association of Hop producers which had endeavoured to market their produce in common. The scheme had failed because it had not covered all the crop and all the producers. It had been torpedoed by blacklegs. But the mass of the growers had already become convinced that they must try and sell things in common, and that they could only do so successfully if the whole of the crop could be dealt with and blacklegging operations made impossible. The second reason that made a Hop Board easy was that it concerned a commodity which had one destination only, the vat. In this case, also, a relatively small number of producers were concerned and experienced merchants had already become convinced of the advantages of dealing with a single responsible organisation.

One might have thought that the proper marketing of fat cattle where the abattoir provides the single and obvious channel to the market would have been arranged already. It would have been if the Labour Government had remained in power and we had been able to proceed with the next stages of the marketing plan. The fact is, however, that, since then, we have had a Government that has, so to say, only applied the Act of 1931 so far as they have been compelled by necessity. The reason why we are still without the necessary scheme for fat cattle is a significant illustration of the power of the interests that are marshalled against an orderly advance. Every auction market, every dealer and every butcher who does his own slaughtering is against it. But even their united opposition would be of little avail if the producers as a whole demanded it. The moral is that an intelligent and determined demand must be mobilised under the leadership of the Government of the day. If that leadership were supplied the response of the industry would undoubtedly be ready and powerful, but you cannot expect initiative in these matters of major policy from hundreds of thousands of separate individual producers.

In order to display the considerations that should be taken account of in framing a scheme to deal efficiently with the marketing of a large-scale commodity and to furnish a guide as to the Powers and Duties that should belong to such an organisation, let us take the difficult case of Egg and Poultry production.

These supplies rank after the production of meat and milk as the next most important home-food product, representing nearly £30,000,000 worth annually and concerning 140,000 separate producers.

Nothing could be more deplorable than the wide fluctuation and uncertainties of price that attach to egg production. The facts have been stated already and reference to them here is only required as pointing to the type of organisation that is required for dealing with marketing.

The spring price of 8d. or 9d. per dozen is too low to give the producer a living, and the autumn price of 2s. 6d. is too high to allow demand to be sustained. In some districts, also, where the egg supply in the local market is in excess of the district demand, the price may be 2d. or 3d. per dozen lower than at some other places on the same day. Any intelligent price-management system must seek to abate these inequalities whilst taking account of demand. In other words, you must have a body well furnished with market intelligence, in touch with distribution agencies and able to control the freakish ups-and-downs of prices and consumption.

Moreover it is of the utmost importance to increase demand, because the consumption of eggs is nothing like as great as it ought to be. So far as children are concerned it ought at least to be twice what it is at present. It is therefore in the interest of consumers and producers alike that we should have a system of price management intelligently directed to sustain demand as well as to safeguard producers' prices. Up to a certain level of price the public is prepared to buy eggs freely and they are always willing to give more for reliable new-laid eggs than for other eggs. They are worth it. At the same time there are few commodities which are more readily given up or displaced by other foods when prices reach a level which puts the brake on bulk consumption.

Matters affecting imported supplies will be dealt with later, but it happens that the monthly importation of eggs from different parts of the world is remarkably even. At the present time home-produced supplies represent about 55 per cent of what we consume, subject, as already explained, to a wide variation between spring and autumn supplies. In addition to this, a spell of unfavourable or favourable weather during either season will have a marked effect upon the home supplies coming forward, and any Board that is in charge of operations must have direct and prompt information as to the supplies likely to be available.

Here, then, is a commodity produced by a great number of producers all over the country subject to wide seasonal variations, always marketed very disadvantageously to the producers in the spring, and specially subject to prices rapidly affecting demand.

How would a Producers' Board in a case like this proceed to introduce a reliable price system? In order to be successful it must be able to prevent the excessive fall in spring prices which has been ruinous to many producers and abate the exaggeration of price that occurs in the autumn and winter with its destructive effect upon demand. This can only be done if the Board is both well supplied with market intelligence and possesses control over the supplies.

The unholy scramble to get rid of eggs anyhow, as is the case in many districts during the spring season, clearly must be dealt with. This could be done in two ways; first by diverting the eggs from the districts of surplus to where they are wanted, and, second, if there is a general glut, being able to store a sufficient percentage under the best conditions. Only the best eggs can be properly stored; and there is a good market for good preserved eggs. The percentage of spring supplies during, say, February, March and a part of April that could advantageously be stored might perhaps represent about 8 per cent of the total supplies that would come forward during that period. In some weeks of unfavourable weather none would be stored. In glut weeks 10 or even 12 per cent might perhaps be stored. These preserved eggs would be released to the market from August onwards at the price which would cover the cost when put down plus storage costs. The spring prices at which eggs were released to the market would be kept as low as would be fair to the producers not only for the purpose of sustaining demand but in order to provide for the profitable marketing of the preserved eggs when released.

This means that the Board would have to be equipped with sufficient storage facilities and be in a position, *every day*, to divert eggs from a surplus region to a region requiring them or to store a percentage as the case may be. From this it follows that the eggs themselves must pass through a channel over which the Board itself has control.

These channels would be egg-packing stations. Those that exist at present, as well as others that would require to be established, would be under the authority of the Board. This does not necessarily mean that the ownership of the present packing stations need be altered, but it does mean that the operations of all the packing stations would be under the authority of the Board to a sufficient extent.

There would need to be sensible arrangements for maintaining direct supply from producer to consumer where it is most convenient, but the licenses issued for this purpose would require observance of the established price system.

In a commodity like eggs it would, probably, not be possible at first to prescribe more than a weekly price. As the machinery got into working order and experience developed it would be possible to fix prices for longer periods.

In this connection it would be necessary that the weekly price would be a *National* price and not different as between one region and another. At the present time there are wide differences in the prices in the different districts; low, say, in Cornwall and Devon and other exporting areas, and higher in others which are near a big market. Unless the stated price was the same throughout all regions there would be a conflict of interest between the different regions and management would become impossible. This could be dealt with by making the uniform weekly fixed-price to be that at which the eggs were *delivered to the wholesalers' premises* and deducting the extra cost of transport from the net price paid to the producer in the exporting regions. The wholesalers would require to be assured of regular and sound supplies and it would be the business of the Board to arrange not only for the distribution of excesses from producing regions to the nearest or most appropriate consuming centres, but to be responsible for the soundness of the supplies.

An essential concomitant of the scheme would therefore be uniform and satisfactory testing, grading and packing to suit the requirements of the wholesalers and of the public.

It would be necessary also to secure that the producers would benefit by any economics that could be effected through an organised system of collection and distribution as well as by improved selling methods. The costs of these services at different packing stations would be deducted from the national weekly price, and producers would receive in an appropriate way, a report not only of the costs at their own packing station, but at others. It would be the business of the Board, on behalf of the producers, to apply, so far as possible, the good lessons that might be learnt in one area for the benefit of another so as to

achieve economies in standardisation, in the supply of packing materials, in handling methods and in other directions.

In addition to these services, if the producers were
satisfied that the Board was giving efficient management,
they would soon look to it for help in the purchase of
feeding-stuffs instead of obtaining them in the present
happy-go-lucky and expensive manner. I have had the
advantage of seeing in a small way the services which central
buying can provide by my membership of the Markets' Committee of the Land Settlement Association. This Committee
made arrangements for purchase and distribution, through
central machinery, of the supplies of feeding-stuffs for the pigs
and poultry kept by the settlers. It relates at present only to
a small number of people, less than 2,000 in all, but without revealing details, one can say with confidence that large
reductions on current market prices are obtainable and that,
with wise direction, the business could be managed with the
goodwill of the Millers' Organisations.

Finally, so far as the individual producer is concerned,
the system *must be simple and convenient*. The aim of a marketing
organisation of this kind should be to place every premium
upon the producer concentrating his thoughts and energies
upon his work as a producer and to relieve him of the
anxieties and uncertainties which attach to the marketing of
his produce in which he is at such a disadvantage. The eggs
would be collected weekly, or oftener if required, and the producer paid at the same time for his previous week's supplies.
He would have no bad debts and no costs of collection.

It is not necessary to duplicate for Poultry the kind of
considerations we have been taking account of in the
case of eggs. They are different, of course, but on the whole
somewhat less difficult. Those who are interested will find
them set out in the report of the Reorganisation Commission for Eggs and Poultry which was published in 1934.

The Report on poultry, however, does bring out in a very
striking fashion other valuable services which a Producers'
Board might render. It is possible that as many poultry producers have been ruined through disease and through being

supplied with defective stock as they have been by low egg prices in the spring. The annual loss of the industry from disease is about £4,000,000 per annum, or something like 13 per cent of the value of its produce in eggs and poultry.

The losses arising out of the supply of infected or weakly stock have long been known throughout the industry; and many of them could undoubtedly be prevented by the control and supervision of the supplies of day-old chicks. Our national expenditure in the prevention and eradication of the diseases which have these appalling results is about £10,000 in all! Under the Agricultural Marketing Act as now wisely amended (1933) Producers' Boards are authorised not only to assist, but, if need be, to arrange for the conduct of research; and, in the absence of other provision, a Producers' Board would not be long in existence before it took effective steps to assist its members in this respect.

In this connection, however, it is really gratifying to record the results of the investigations of a technical Committee under Sir Duncan Watson that was set up by the Minister of Agriculture as a result of the recommendations of the Reorganisation Commission.

The Report of this Technical Committee was received in January 1938[1] and it is to be hoped that the Government will lose no time in giving effect to its recommendations.

The picture they present is even worse than one could have anticipated. They recommend the appointment of an independent Poultry (Stock Improvement) Commission for Great Britain as a National Body with wide powers and duties.

It is not necessary to repeat their recommendations in detail, but in effect they require:—

1. The compulsory registration of every distributor of stock, hatching eggs, and day-old chicks.
2. The observance of good conditions under the licence of the Commission.
3. The institution of grading and testing.

[1] Report of the Poultry Technical Committee for Gt. Britain, 1936. Price 1s.

4. The control over conditions of auction and other sales.
5. The assistance of research, and general supervision.

If the Government will only give effect to these far-reaching proposals it will confer a great benefit upon the industry, although it will have to face, at the outset, the opposition of those undesirables whose operations have been so much responsible for the present conditions.

So far as the plan of operations I am recommending is concerned, the only result would be that the National Commission would find, ready to hand, an independent National body in existence competent to act on its behalf in these matters just as it is hoped the Live Stock Commission will be able to do in the case of cattle.

In conclusion on Producers Boards, first-rate management is essential. Marketing Boards are not to be regarded as places for making jobs for friends. They call for the best administrative and management talent that can be obtained, and it is well worth while paying for. It is no good pretending that in the world today the highly skilled management that is required can be obtained on the cheap. It cannot. The cost in the case of a scheme for eggs and poultry, distributed over the whole industry, is trivial. It was estimated by the Reorganisation Commission[1] at less than 1 per cent and, ultimately, that the total costs would be less than the amounts now paid by producers for service charges at Packing Stations.

Powers of Producer's Boards

It is now appropriate to gather together from the foregoing a summary of the kind of Powers and Duties that should attach to such a Board.

1. It should have such control over the sale of the producer's product that it can establish a reliable price system which will give confidence both to the

[1] See the Report of the Reorganisation Commission for Eggs and Poultry, 1934. Economic Series, Ministry of Agriculture, No. 42, pages 121 and 125.

producers and to the distributive market that will receive the supply.

2. It should have power to arrange for suitable storage if necessary.

3. It should be able to arrange for regular and methodical supply of the market in accordance with the needs of the market.

4. It should be able to take steps to encourage demand both by improving the character, standard, grading and convenience of supply as well as by propaganda of an appropriate kind.

5. It should be able to obtain and disseminate good market intelligence.

6. It should be able to encourage, by price premiums and otherwise, improved methods of production.

7. It should be able to arrange, where appropriate, for the utilisation of by-products.

8. It should be able to assist its members in regard to the supply of Feeding-stuffs, appliances and other requirements.

9. It should be able to organise and improve transport, and otherwise diminish costs in market supply.

10. It should be able, so far as necessary, to employ expert assistance and to give help and advice to its members.

11. In addition to these, the Producers' Boards, either on their own account or in co-operation with the National Commission, should be able to help their members in respect of insurance, short-term credit, and kindred matters.

12. In the same way it should be able to assist or co-operate with the other authorities in connection with the spread of information, research, veterinary and other services.

13. Finally, a Board's help might be required in connection with schemes designed by the National Commission for improved land cultivation, extension of specialised production and other projects, including co-operation with the National Government in connection with the provision of cheap food supplies—milk in schools, and other experiments of a like character.

Finally, comment should be made upon one development of the use of Home Producers' Marketing Boards that has taken place since 1933.

Our intention in framing the Agricultural Marketing Act of 1931 was that the function of Producers' Boards should be limited (so far as sales were concerned) to the primary sales of the products to the market.

The business of Distribution and retail prices is not, and ought not to be a function of Producers' Boards.

Moreover these Boards should not have *final power* with regard to price determination. It will never do to allow any section of producers to have power to hold up the Community to ransom. I shall return to this subject when considering the powers of the National Commission in regard to price, but, short of some such over-riding control in the national interests, Producers' Boards should be in a position to arrange all the price conditions attaching to primary sales.

The fact that the Act of 1931 has not been followed by the provision of appropriate powers with regard to Imports and Distribution costs has had most unfortunate results. The most conspicuous at the moment is supplied by the Milk Marketing Board, which, in order to get an agreement with the Distributors, has had to become a party to an increase in the retail prices of milk. They have been forced into this position by the absence of any other authority capable of dealing with Distribution, but it is of first-rate importance that the powers of Producer's Boards, in regard to sales, should attach only to primary sales and not go beyond that point. Otherwise, as is now the case, they may become entangled in controversies and difficulties which are outside their sphere. Their business and interests are those of the Producer, and the presentation of his product to the market in the most acceptable and convenient form. They are not constituted for purposes outside these. The complicated machinery of Distribution is for others to deal with; it presents altogether different problems and calls for an entirely different type of experience and personnel.

PART II

SECTION VI

Chapter XII

The Control of Imports

Objects of Import Control—Duties of the Controlling Authority—
The Reports of Various Commissions—Objections Raised in 1930
—Need for Control in the People's Interest—War-time Experience.

THE CONTROL OF Imports by the State in one
form or another has been greatly extended in this country
during the past six years.

Those who have read the previous chapters will not
require to ask why the control of Imports is needed, but
it is well to keep our chief objectives in mind. They are:

First, to secure that the food supply of the people is
abundant, and liberated from any artificial restrictions
or manipulations that are against the public interest.

Second, to get rid, so far as possible, of uncertainties
of price and be able to place upon a firm foundation a
system that will give sufficient security of price for the
home-producer. And,

Third, to effect such economies in storage, distribution
and other services as large-scale management may enable
us to obtain.

In brief; the aim should be to place the food supplies
of the people upon a secure basis, to make sure that they
are abundant and at the same time give confidence to those
who cultivated the land at home.

Unless an Import Board, or whatever it may be called,
can contribute substantially towards the attainment of
these ends there is no reason for creating it.

An important use of Import Control, so far as Home
Agriculture is concerned, would be, through its co-operation
with the corresponding Home Board, the promotion of
stability in the price of the home-produced commodity

KA

concerned. The method adopted would necessarily be
different in different commodities. Where the commodity
was one in which we were largely dependent on importation, such as wheat and flour, beef, bacon, butter, wool
and some others, the assistance that Import Board could
render would be greater than when, as in the case of milk
or potatoes, the bulk of our supplies are home-produced
and the Home Board itself might be sufficiently effective
within its own domain. These considerations are important
in determining the order in which the system would be
introduced.

In a later chapter I will try to give some illustrations of
how the necessary co-operation between Home and
Import Boards might be obtained, but before that stage
is reached we must consider the relevant requirements of
Import Control itself in some detail.

An Import Control System might be operated either
through a separate Board or Corporation, or by means
of an Authority that would work through the issue of
licences to which appropriate conditions would be attached.

When a separate Board or Corporation was created it
would require to have its own Seal, Finance and Authority
and be able to arrange directly for Purchases, Transport,
Insurance, Storage and other matters.

It will probably be found, however, especially as things
have now developed, that the most convenient method of
approach for most commodities would be by the establishment of an Import Control Agency that would operate
through existing trade channels by a system of licences.

In any case, to discharge efficiently the duties imposed
upon it the Importing Authority would require:—

1. To be established on a commodity or group-commodity
   basis.
2. To have complete control over the import of all the
   commodity or commodities concerned.
3. To be able to promote economies in insurance, transport,
   storage, and the like.

4. To be able to promote economies in marketing, by the elimination of margins and otherwise.
5. To operate so as to cover expenses, but not to aim at making a profit.
6. To have a licensing authority that would cover the issue of licences in trade for re-export as well as for trade at home.

With this summary before us let us review the historical and other considerations that are relevant.

It is well known that at the Imperial Conference in 1930 Mr. Bruce, the Prime Minister of Australia, was anxious that a National Purchase Corporation should be established for the bulk purchase of Dominion supplies, especially of meat, wheat and wool. This was ruled out at the time by the kind of opposition of which we saw a good example in the evidence that Sir Maurice Hankey offered before the Arms Commission Enquiry in regard to the suggestion that the State should be responsible for armament supply. It was not based upon experience, but rather upon a conjuring up of future possible difficulties accompanied by a convenient disregard of the actual circumstances that had given rise to the appointment of the Commission itself.

Some of the opposition offered to Mr. Bruce's proposal was based upon the assumption that arguments founded upon war-time experience were not relevant, but no reasons were given for this amazing contention.

We have had a series of Government Commissions of one sort or another on Food-Supply questions. They have considered the facts as they found them in peace-time, and have also taken account of the lessons of war-time practice and experience. Without exception they have reported favourably upon the work that was done during the war and have derived suggestions therefrom.

The reader who is interested should refer to these reports. They will be found to be enlightening not only upon past experience, but upon what is now happening under Quantitative Regulation.

The Reports are:—

1. The Departmental Committee on Distribution and Prices of Agricultural Produce (Lord Linlithgow).
2. The Report of the Committee on the Stabilisation of Agricultural Prices, 1925.
3. The Inter-Departmental Committee on Meat Supplies, Cmd. 456, 1919 (Bridgeman Report).
4. The Interim Report on Meat from the Sub-Committee appointed by the Standing Committee on Trusts, Cmd. 1057, 1920 (Macrosty Report).
5. The First Report of the Royal Commission on Food Prices, Cmd. 2390, 1925 (Sir Auckland Geddes' Report).
6. The First Report of the Royal Commission on Wheat Supplies, Cmd. 1544, 1921 (The Rt. Hon. Earl of Crawford and Balcarres).
7. The Trading Accounts and Balance Sheets 1920–21 with the Reports of the Controller and Auditor-General, No. 126, 1922.

To some people the expression "Import Board" has become a sort of bogey. But if we look into the facts we shall find that the present Wheat Commission, the controls now exercised under the authority of the Imports Advisory Committee and the Meat Committees that will be established under the Livestock Act go a considerable distance towards performing many of the duties that would fall to any corresponding Import Board. After all, it does not matter what we call it. What matters is what it does and the purposes for which it does it. So far, however, as many of the chief objections that were urged against Import Boards in 1930 are concerned, the difficulties that were then recited must have been experienced by those who have had charge of Quantitative Regulation during the past six years, except that, apart from Wheat, the experiments of the last few years have left the question of price untouched save by sporadic attempts to bolster up prices by restriction of supply.

One of the chief objections urged in 1930 was that, as a result of the State becoming involved in bulk purchases, either directly or by authorising transactions by others, we might become involved in difficulties with the Dominions or with Foreign Nations. Also it was claimed that such operations would cut across existing Treaties.

It is perfectly true, of course, that State Control over Food Importation, however it is exercised, will involve negotiations and agreements with the Dominions as well as with other Governments. But what reason have we to suppose that the responsible and experienced men who would be in charge of the negotiations would not be able to conduct them successfully and with goodwill?

People who bring objections like this to State intervention in these affairs must be living with their heads in the sand. They must also have had them pretty deeply buried, because they must have lost sight of what has been happening since 1932. Quantitative Regulation has involved the alteration of Trade Agreements with Governments all over the world. The agreement that was entered into at Ottawa has rendered inter-Governmental negotiations even more complicated than they might otherwise have been. The compulsory Regulation of Imports of chilled and frozen beef, of bacon and ham, beef and veal, potatoes, eggs and other commodities has involved widespread alteration of Treaties and Trade Agreements.

This extensive interference with importation has been dealt with by State Departments. It could not have been otherwise. It is the State that has allocated the imports of bacon and ham between different countries and which has cut down the imports from foreign countries from more than $11\frac{1}{2}$ million cwts. in 1932 to little more than 5 million in 1936. It is the State that arranged for the allocation of a given proportion of these imports to Denmark which has reduced the total amount nearly by half. It is the State that has entered into agreements with the Dominions affecting food importation in all manner of directions, so that we now find a whole series of new

Trade Agreements and modified Treaties, some of which
are terminable at short notice.[1]

But these things have been arranged with much less
friction than would have been created if they had been
the subject of bargaining between conflicting Corporations.
Of course it is the business of the State to handle these
matters. Whatever may be said as to the methods and purpose of these operations it is manifest that the system of
Quantitative Regulation to which the Government is now
committed has knocked the bottom completely out of the
objection that the State should not interfere in these
matters. It always was moonshine; and never had any
relation to reality. Surely we would rather that vital
questions affecting the food supply of the people were
dealt with by the responsible men whom the State employs
than that we were left to the tender mercies of the Meat
Trust and other Corporations.

In this connection some facts elicited by the different
Commissions already referred to are worth attention. The
Bridgman Committee and the Royal Commission on Food
Prices provided much enlightenment upon the operations
of the Corporations that are concerned with meat and
wheat supplies. We were told, for instance, that 88 per cent
of the supplies of Argentine beef were controlled by two
great Corporations. There was no rivalry in purchase
between them; there was no rivalry in selling; on the contrary, there was "a harmonious interchange of ideas on
the subject of price". One alone of these great concerns
controls a large proportion of our Cold Storage as well
as the operations of some 2,400 shops. Moreover a "freight
Committee" sitting regularly in London controls the
amount of freight that is to be allowed. Is it better that
this Freight Committee should decide how much meat
we are to have than that the matter should be the business
of a responsible national authority?

[1] Readers will find an excellent summary of these new Trade Agreements in the *Agricultural Register*, 1936-7, Chapter V. Pub. by the
Agricultural Economic Research Institute, Oxford.

The Committee on Food Prices over which Sir Auckland Geddes presided came to this conclusion:—[1]

> "The system of regulating supplies of an important article of food by a combination of private traders is open to serious criticism on grounds of public policy. It is not a system which either producers or consumers can be expected to view without grave suspicion, and in the long run we believe that both producers and consumers will demand a controlling influence in the administration and policy of trading organisations exercising these vast powers."

Although this Royal Commission—which reported seven years before Quantitative Regulation was introduced—was not prepared to go so far as to recommend a "State Monopoly", they did go so far as to say—even with that possibility in mind—that they "would view with still greater reluctance a complete lack of effective supervision."[2]

Apart, however, from safeguards against private monopoly and any artificial scarcity it might be responsible for, we want a Body that will enable us to get some reasonable stability into Prices. Our food supplies should be emancipated from the influence of the "bulls and the bears". In other words, we want a system that will give confidence to British Agriculture as well as to consumers.

In this connection the report on the Stabilisation of Agricultural Prices is an exceptionally valuable document. The Report gives Chapter and Verse for the conclusion that "uncertainty of price" had long been one of the chief disabilities of the British Farmer. It insisted that price stability on a satisfactory level is rightly becoming part of the social ideal towards which the public will and conscience are moving. The Report also provides some illuminating illustrations of the ups and downs of price that even small surpluses may give rise to under present conditions, and of their desolating effects. The Bridgeman Committee,

[1] Royal Commission on Food Prices, par 293, p. 118.
[2] *Ibid.*, par 334, p. 135.

as well as this Committee, also furnished disconcerting
evidence of the unnecessary increases of cost that are
often associated with multiple dealings. The Committee
on the Stabilization of Prices concluded that "the problem
before this country is how long it can afford to ignore
these conditions which in their reactions on British markets
may exert so profound an influence."[1]

If action is to be taken, it can only be by the acceptance
of another finding of the same Committee that "in our
opinion it would be impossible to devise a system of
orderly marketing of imports on lines which would,
at once, protect British Agriculture from the consequences
of fluctuations in world prices and British markets from
domination by foreign organisations, except through
participation, or at least supervision, by the State. We
do not see any escape from this conclusion".[2] There is none.

As already said, there need be nothing set or stereotyped about the form that "supervision" would take.
It would necessarily vary with the methods of importation
and passage on to the market of different commodities,
as well as be affected by the form which the various
arrangements now being established have come to possess.
Whilst it is undoubtedly true that, if those who are like-
minded with myself had continued in power after 1931,
we should have instituted arrangements profoundly
different in many respects from those that are now coming
into operation, the way is being made easier every year.
Consolidation under some form or other of State supervision is proceeding apace, and traders and State Departments alike are becoming more and more accustomed to
these new practices.

At the same time, in considering the form of any future
organisation, it would be stupid to ignore the lessons that
can be learnt from the immensely rich experience that
was gained during the war. The methods of management

[1] Report of the Committee on the Stabilization of Agricultural Prices,
Par. 115, p. 167.
[2] Ibid., Par. 117, pp. 67–8.

then instituted were very various. In some cases, as under the Commission that had charge of Wheat Supplies, there was an organisation operating directly on behalf of the State which successfully carried through transactions of a prodigious character for several years. It brought into its service (as would happen in any case) the best ability and experience that could be mobilised. It safeguarded us against exploitation, and even in those perilous times, by its co-operation with the Ministries of Food and Shipping, ensured a remarkable regularity of supply. Its transactions amounted to £1,400,000,000. It imported about ten million tons of wheat or flour each year; it supervised the distributions through trade channels, at established margins, to 40,000 bakers and to 100,000 retailers, and its operating costs over the whole period were only 1s. 2d. per £100, or one-seventeenth of 1 per cent.

Quite different arrangements were instituted to safeguard meat supplies. Amongst other operations undertaken as a part of this work, was the acquisition and management of some large meat works at Las Palmas, and it is interesting to recall that this enterprise was found to be so valuable that it was continued for three years after the war. It would have been carried on even longer if the recommendation of the Macrosty Committee in 1920 had been adopted. "That the Las Palmas meat works in Argentina should continue to be operated on behalf of His Majesty's Government so as to afford a means of watching the developments of cost and price movements."[1] Not only was that great concern found to be valuable in safeguarding us against price exploitation and fluctuation, but it was so well-managed that the Accountant and Auditor-General in his report for 1920-21 states that "the profits at 31st March 1921 of the frozen meat factory at Las Palmas amounted to £617,695".

In a great variety of other ways also, under the authority of the War Office and the Ministry of Munitions, there was State Management of importation—alongside control

[1] Recommendation No. 4, p. 13.

of the price of a large number of commodities—wool, hides, flax, jute, hemp, and many minerals and chemicals. The Controller and Auditor-General in the Trading Accounts and Balance Sheets for 1920–21 reported that these importations and sales under the control of the two War departments had resulted in profits of more than £27 million being surrendered to the Exchequer apart from repayments to the Dominions of more than £5 million and to India of nearly £8½ million.

We may all hope that there will never again be an occasion for the institution of the drastic rationing and control that the Ministry of Food had to exercise, but it is childish to pretend that, when in times of dire necessity we were able to conduct the control of food supplies through that State Department with transactions exceeding £1,200 million at an administrative cost of less than 1 per cent, there are not some lessons to be learnt[1] which we might usefully employ in the public interests in times of peace.

I was one of those who happened to be behind the scenes and to have a share in much of this business, and I confess that when I remember something of the exploitation that State Management saved us from in those days, I have not much patience with some of the theoretical and entirely pettifogging objections that were put forward in 1930 by people who had never had any part or lot in it. Some of these people seemed to imagine that the only form of Import Control required to obtain the ends we have in view, would be some sort of soulless, State-Monopoly Monster managed by doctrinaires swathed in red tape. We have in this country an unrivalled wealth of men experienced in these matters and it would be the State's business to make use of them in appropriate ways; and it is as certain as can be that, with the right methods of approach and management, this experienced assistance could be enlisted.

[1] Readers who are interested in what was done in those days, and how it was done, are advised to read *Experiments in State Control*, by E. M. H. Lloyd, the Clarendon Press.

We were told in 1930 that the State Monopoly the objectors imagined, might be tempted to "sell at a loss and thus subsidise prices at the expense of the taxpayer", or, on the other hand, that it might refuse to sell and so create an artificial shortage and thus inflate prices. It is quite possible, of course, that an Import Control, whatever its form, might make mistakes. But is it likely that, with the grave public responsibilities with which it would be entrusted, it would be as likely to manipulate prices contrary to public interests as the different Trusts and Combinations, whom it would displace or control, might be disposed to do if they were left free to operate on their own account? Indeed, the recognition of the dangers to which the community is exposed in this respect was the chief reason why the different Commissions already referred to made the recommendations they did.

A refusal to recognise that a responsible State authority would fail to supply the needs of the people and at the same time try to diminish the present evils of price uncertainty is to allow prejudice to cloud our judgment and to blind ourselves to ascertained fact.

PART II

SECTION VII

Chapter XIII

The National Commission and Home-Producers' Boards

Objectives and Considerations of Policy—Table of Home-Produced and Imported Supplies—Internal Questions Affecting Home-Producers' Boards—Milk, Beef and Mutton, Bacon and Pig Meat, Eggs and Poultry, Potatoes, Market-garden Produce—Producers' Requirements.

IN OUR LAST two chapters we have dealt with the machinery and powers necessary to obtain sufficient control over the prices and marketing of Home-Produced and Imported supplies. Let us now examine the principal Objectives and Considerations of Policy that would present themselves to the National Commission in making use of the powers provided in connection with the chief commodities.

Governing Considerations

With regard to Objectives: the first point to be emphasised is that it is not so much higher prices that need to be aimed at as stability of price. Many prices are high enough now to provide a good living for an efficient producer if he knew that he could rely upon them. Also the prices paid by the consumer for many supplies contain all, and indeed sometimes more, than is necessary for a fair producers' price if we could eliminate needless increases between the one and the other.

In the second place, the purpose of price stabilization at a fair level is that it may promote a better use of the land. We cannot afford to perpetuate a system whereby land can be put down wholesale to grass and labour dispensed with, simply because it may be easier to carry on and get a living that way instead of by devoting the land to its proper use. The interests of the State must over-ride the immediate convenience of an occupier who pursues such a policy. It is perfectly true that improved organisations and machinery will lead to a more economical use of labour upon a given area of land, but they may equally well be used for increased production and increased employment. Price Management, indeed, will fail of its purpose unless it succeeds in stimulating enterprise, in encouraging the adoption of better management and in the application of improved knowledge. It will be necessary all the time, therefore, to resist the pressure to adopt a system that will provide a low-grade satisfaction and entrench inefficiency.

It follows that the National Commission must have an over-riding direction, both in the interests of national food supply and of land development, of the main operations of Home-Producers and of Import Boards, otherwise we might find that the Boards, established under State Authority, became little better than existing Trusts and Cartels. The present Imports Duties Advisory Committee does in some measure represent a small degree of State Control in so far as it requires to be satisfied when interested parties come before it asking for Tariffs; but if we are to have a Body that can plan a great scheme of Land Development, with all that that involves, it must be one that has a continually directing power. The National Agricultural Commission equipped with such authority will work through the County Committees as well as through the appropriate Commodity Boards in planning increased home production.

At the present time, also, other developments are proceeding apace. The Livestock Commission will soon be in a position to effect improvements in Cattle Marketing. It is to be hoped that the Bacon Development Board will produce order out of the existing confusion in Pig Marketing, and there are other important bodies such as the Wheat and Sugar Commissions. These new authorities make it the more important that a consolidated machinery of direction should be created.

As a parenthesis I may here refer back to what was previously insisted on, namely, that the Duties of Home-Producers' Boards, so far as sales are concerned, should

not extend beyond "Primary Sales" to the market. When
we have regard to the important questions of policy that
must belong to any considered national scheme it is
evident that Producers' Boards are not fitted to deal
with them. They are not constituted for such purposes.
There is an abundant and magnificent field of work for
them in looking after the interests of the Producer and in
promoting the efficiency and success of Production as
such, and it is to be deplored that, in the absence of any
other machinery, they are being forced into accepting
responsibilities which are beyond their sphere.

With regard to its Price operations in general, the
National Commission would aim, in the first instance, at
ironing out fluctuations in prices and enabling the
appropriate Board to establish schemes of fixed prices
over longer and longer terms. In most wholesale operations
the price margin is probably not unreasonably high,
although sometimes there is a needless duplication of
such operations. The big gap is between the wholesale and
the retail price, and if the Commission is to be successful
it must have power to promote appropriate arrangements
for obtaining economies in distribution processes.

In the light of these general considerations let us review
the operations that would be required of the National
Commission in regard to the price management of the
different major commodities. For the time being I will
omit cereal crops—wheat, barley and oats—because the
cultivation of them is so intimately bound up with plans
for future development that they are better dealt with
in that connection, except that the plan that has been
adopted for wheat prices must be referred to.

So far as possible the following order will be adopted
in the remainder of this Chapter and in the next, although
some degree of overlapping is unavoidable:—

1. Internal questions affecting Home-Producers' Prices.
2. The Purchase of Producers' Requirements.
3. Importation.

4. Distribution.
5. The means whereby the Labourer must be assured of his share of the benefits.

The accompanying table of home-produced and imported food supplies, for the last completed year that is analysed, is relevant to what follows:

HOME-PRODUCED AND IMPORTED SUPPLIES

UNITED KINGDOM

June 1935—May 1936. (From the *Agricultural Register* 1936–37) with some later figures supplied by the Ministry of Agriculture. The Milk figures are supplied by the Milk Marketing Board for Oct. 1935—Nov. 1936.

	HOME-PRODUCED	IMPORTED	PERCENTAGE HOME-PRODUCED
Cereals	Cwts.	Cwts.	
Wheat	31,640,000	112,312,000	21·9
Barley	14,640,000	17,107,000	46
Oats	36,360,000	1,038,000	91
Meat (*a*)	Cwts.	Cwts.	
Beef and Veal	12,790,000	12,846,000	50
Mutton and Lamb	4,849,000	6,502,780	43·6
Pig Meat	8,206,000	8,742,163	48·4
Potatoes	Tons	Tons	
	3,041,000	309,773	90·7
Eggs	Millions	Millions	
Eggs (in shell)	3,347	2,653	55·7
Eggs (liquid and dried)	—	Cwts. 823,643	Nil
Poultry	Cwts.	Cwts.	
	1,489,000	422,117	77
Milk	Galls. of Milk	Galls. of Milk	
Milk (for liquid consumption)	773,400,000	Nil	100

	HOME-PRODUCED	IMPORTED	PERCENTAGE HOME-PRODUCED
Milk Products (b)	Milk Galls. equiv.	Milk Galls. equiv.	
Butter	146,900,000	2,506,900,000	5·8
Cheese	124,600,000	287,300,000	30·2
Other Products	165,000,000	40,100,000	80·5
Fresh Fruit (c)	Cwts.	Cwts.	
1936	12,544,000	7,053,843	68·3
Vegetables and Tomatoes (d)	Estimated Value	Estimated Value	
	£25,015,000	£5,429,000	82
Sugar (Refined) (e)	Cwts.	Cwts.	
	11,045,226	27,396,804	28·7

Notes

(a) There were also imports of 695,000 live cattle; 455,000 live sheep; 120,721 live pigs.

(b) The Milk Board has kindly converted the imported supplies into the equivalent gallons of milk which are thus comparable with the Home-Production figures.

The gallonage of milk in Col. 1 is in addition to the milk made into butter, on the farms. If this is allowed for, it is estimated that the home-production percentage (Col. 3) might be raised to 9 per cent or thereabouts.

(c) Pears, Plums, Cherries, Strawberries, Raspberries, Black and other Currants, and Gooseberries. Imported fruits, such as Bananas, Peaches, Apricots, Nuts and various other fruits not akin to these produced at home, are omitted.

(d) *Vegetables.* The quantity produced is not known. The acreage devoted to market-garden vegetables was 250,171 in addition to 1,726 for tomatoes. The value is according to official estimates. The import figures refer to Tomatoes and Onions only.

Tomatoes. The imports of tomatoes in 1935 were 2,830,416 cwts.

Onions. The amount of home-produced Onions marketed in England and Wales was 3,800 cwts. The imports of Onions were 10,430,628 cwts.

(e) These figures are for the amounts retained for home consumption.

INTERNAL QUESTIONS AFFECTING HOME-PRODUCERS'
PRICES

Milk

In terms of cash returns this is at the top of the list and may be taken first. When we come to examine the different destinations of the milk we see that there are two main problems to be dealt with—the Consumption of Liquid Milk and the small proportion of Butter produced at home.

The total production of milk in the United Kingdom, October 1935 to September 1936, according to figures kindly supplied to me by the Milk Marketing Board, was 1,209 million gallons.

This milk was used as follows:—

	Million gallons	Per cent
For Liquid Consumption	773·4	63·9
Factory Manufacture	410·6	33·9
Farmhouse Cheese	25·9	2·2
	1,209·9	100

The Prices paid to the Producers, excluding what the producer had himself to pay for Transport, were as follows:—

	Pence per Gallon
For Liquid Consumption	14·97
For Manufacture	5·48
Average Return to Producer before Paying Transport	11·22

I have not been able to obtain an average figure for the cost of Transport for Great Britain, but the Milk Marketing Board has supplied me with figures for England and Wales. These countries supplied 83 per cent of the milk

LA

and received a somewhat higher price, so that the result to the producer for Great Britain would be a little less.

The Figures for England and Wales are as follows:—

	Million Gallons		Price per Gallon Pence
For Liquid Consumption	665·3	Liquid	15·23
For Manufacture	342·4	Manufactured	5·45
Farmhouse Cheese	17·7		
Total	1,025·4	Average return	11·48

The Net return to the producer is arrived at as follows:—

	Pence
Average Return	11·48
Special Services and Quality Bonuses	·38
	11·86
Less Transport Charges	1·73
Net Return to Producer	10·13

In connection with Transport charges, the Milk Marketing Board makes the following note:—

"The weighted average Transport charges vary in the respective regions, and the range is from round about 1d. to 2½d. per gallon. The average transport charges for individual producers vary from ½d. to 3¼d. per gallon."

The figures exclude sales of milk by the Producer Retailers but they represent the state of affairs so far as the bulk of producers are concerned.

The chief reason why 410 million gallons of milk in Great Britain went to manufacture was because the liquid milk market, at the prevalent retail prices, was not able to take more than it did.

According to an arrangement made by the Central Milk Distributors' Committee and the Milk Marketing Board in August 1937, the retail price in London for four months in the year was to be thirty pence per gallon, twenty-eight pence for five months, and twenty-four pence for the other three months. There are some provincial and other variations, but it is fair to say that, for the bulk of the population, milk will cost twenty-eight pence per gallon, or more, for nine months in the year, and twenty-four pence per gallon for the remainder.

The price of milk sent to manufacture is determined according to a formula that takes into account the price of imported butter, and the result of this deflection of an immense volume of milk to manufacture at $5\frac{1}{2}d.$ per gallon is that the average return to the producer is reduced to little more than $11d.$ out of which he has to pay transport. In any case, however, the retail price is from about $1s.$ to $1s.$ $3d.$ per gallon higher than the price paid to the producer even if we disregard deductions on account of manufactured milk. All the time the outstanding need of the people is to increase consumption of liquid milk.

The first task, therefore, for the Commission would be to promote a rational system of distribution that would reduce this outrageous charge of a shilling a gallon for a few hours' operations in bottling, cleaning and distribution, so as to enable retail prices to be reduced and increased consumption to be encouraged. This will be considered under Distribution in the next chapter together with the Import Policy problems arising out of the disproportion in the amounts of Home-produced and Imported Butter.

Beef and Mutton

These approach milk in money value and nobody would pretend that the prices paid for meat retail do not contain, as a rule, a sufficient reward for the Producer if he got it. It is not necessary to repeat here the case set out with regard to abattoirs in Chapters VII and X, pages 90, and 127–9. Two things clearly are required: first, prices should be much more stabilised by sustained and disinterested management, and, second, the producer should receive, in addition to the standard market price, the enhanced value (estimated at a minimum of £2 3s. 4d. per head for cattle) that would be derivable from a properly conducted abattoir system.

So far as mutton is concerned, we have not yet been provided with the results of a careful enquiry as in the case of beef, but it is common knowledge that when, some years ago, the price of sheep was very low, we did not find it reflected in the price of legs of mutton. It would be the business of the Commission to undertake the enquiries necessary for the promotion of a proper abattoir system for sheep as for cattle, and to exercise their powers to stabilise the prices of the different grades of sheep. The fall in price from 1937–8 is a good Example of the sort of thing that would be guarded against.

These duties would be exercised through the Livestock Commission. At the same time the powers of that Commission would require to be extended so as to cover the promotion of improved marketing arrangements for holding-stock as well as for control of retail margins.

Bacon and Pig Meat

The troubles of the Pigs and Bacon Marketing Boards have been largely due to the absurd double-barrelled arrangement that was created. To some extent, also, because the farmers did not insist at the start on thoroughly competent management.

The arrangement was that one Board (The Pigs Board) sold pigs that had reached the bacon weight (of 160 lbs. or more) to another Board (the Bacon Board) appointed by Factory interests. The inevitable conflict arose. It was to the interests of the Bacon Board to get the pigs at as low a price as possible for the purpose of their profits; it was not their business to promote the interests of the Producers as such. What happened was this. Producers found that they could often do better by selling their pigs as Pork before they reached the Bacon weight, and the Bacon Board in consequence found itself short of the abundant and regular supply of pigs necessary for efficient factory work.

Another result of the creation of a Board, tied to factory interests rather than to those of the Producer, was that in

order to include as much of the trade as possible, there
was a needless multiplication of bacon factories—sometimes
quite small ones provided by local butchers. All this is
contrary to any sound scheme of Marketing designed to
safeguard Producers' interests and at the same time check
increases of cost between producer and consumer. The
whole arrangement naturally broke down and was referred
for investigation to the Bacon Development Board.

Before referring to the result of this investigation, let me
repeat that, just as for Cattle abattoirs, bacon factory
operations ought to be on a public-service basis designed
to encourage improved production and better catering for
the needs of the consumer. It is shocking that the key
position should have been surrendered as it has. It is the
more to be regretted because in the discussions which took
place at the Ministry in 1931 on a future plan for the
bacon industry, it was evident that it would have been
possible to secure the co-operation of experienced factory
concerns in a sound scheme on a proper basis.

The case for Central Control received significant
support in the recent report of the Food Council to the
Board of Trade. The Council said:[1]—

> "We consider that the present situation emphasises
> the need for control by a more independent body who
> can ensure that contract prices for bacon pigs are as
> high as the curing industry can afford and that such
> prices offer to producers in general a stronger induce-
> ment than do open market dealings."

There we have in a nutshell—and in strong language
for an official document—a statement of the vice of allowing
an organisation that operates solely for private profit to
occupy what can be called the "key position".

The most deplorable result of all that has attended this
dreadful blunder in organisation, alongside the reduction
of supplies by quantitative regulation, has been an inflation
of retail prices and a fall in total consumption.

[1] Report of the Food Council for the year 1936, p.6.

In 1932 the total consumption of Pig Meat (home-produced and imported) was 20,692,000 cwts.; in 1937 it had fallen nearly to 17,000,000 cwts., which represents a decreased consumption per head of the population of 12·6 per cent. The retail price of streaky bacon has risen from 10½d. per lb. in 1932 to 1s. 3¼d. in 1937, an increase that is altogether out of proportion to the small increase in the producer's price. It is the result—and the inevitable result—of failure to control distribution whilst supplies were restricted, and at the same time allowing an interested body to be in control of the market and to continue the operation of the present vicious practice of paying the producer as little as possible and charging the consumer as much as possible.

Furthermore it is absurd to expect that we shall ever get a satisfactory scheme through an organisation that deals only with "bacon" pigs. Why should it be important to have a proper scheme for the slaughter and marketing of pigs that weigh 160 lbs. or more and not have one for those that are under that weight? No satisfactory arrangement can ever be devised unless it covers all the different grades of pigs that are sold for consumption and that fulfils the essential conditions of sound marketing.

The disjointed arrangements that have hitherto prevailed also have meant that nothing has been done to assist the producer in the important matter of purchase of feeding-stuffs. There is no case, except perhaps that of egg-production, which presents a greater need for assistance in the purchase of requirements.

In addition to this, an efficient Board would devote its energies to improvements in quality and type. Danish bacon makes nearly as good a price in the British market as our own because of its high quality and because it is graded and produced in such a way as to meet the requirements of the British housewife. Moreover, by Scientific Management and common direction in the Producers' interests the cost of curing Danish Bacon are less than half those alleged to be necessary in this country.

If the British producer were similarly helped, he could

soon defy competition. Once a Producers' Board of the right kind were brought into being and the factory operations placed on a public-utility basis it would be easy for the National Commission to fix ex-bacon factory prices and to control market margins.

In the light of these observations on the principles which should apply to any sound scheme, whatever may be the titles of the bodies administering it, let me refer to the proposals that have emerged as a result of the investigations of the Bacon Development Board and which are embodied in the Bacon Industry Bill introduced into Parliament on April 1st, 1938.

At this time I can only comment upon the chief features of the Bill as submitted to Parliament, but it is probably safe to say that it will pass into law with its main essentials unaltered.

Under the proposals of the Bill, the separate Pigs (or Farmers') Board and the Bacon (or Curers') Board remain, and a new Bacon Development Board with considerable powers is brought into existence.

A standard price of 12s. 6d. per 20 lbs. is assured for the producer for 2,100,000 pigs in the first year with small variations for a greater number in the two succeeding years. Provisions are also made for payments to be adjusted according to alterations in the cost of feeding-stuffs, and there are other valuable proposals for promoting improvements, if they can be given effect to. It is estimated that the price arrangements, which will be supported by the Treasury, may call for a contribution of £1,000,000 in a full year.

But the key position of the Factory interests is maintained; and, indeed, except for the provision that will be mentioned later, appears to be fortified. A Factory Rationalisation Scheme is to be prepared either by the Development Board or by the Bacon Board, but in any case the Bacon Board is the final arbiter. The scheme is to be promoted in the form of an Order by the Minister of Agriculture which will have to be approved by Parliament, but the Minister himself may not submit the Order to Parliament unless the Bacon Board "within twenty-eight days, or such longer time as the Minister may allow that Board, has by Resolution approved the draft".[1]

It is an amazing surrender to a powerful interest. There are no proposals for safeguarding the public in respect to retail prices although the price at which the Factories will obtain their supplies is defined. It can only result in the consolidation and strengthening of the factory interests; and, seeing that the Bill also provides for Quantitative Regulation of Imports, we may confidently look for a continuation of high retail prices and diminished consumption.

There is, however, one safeguard, although under existing conditions one cannot expect much from it. It is that the Powers of a Producers' Board under the Marketing Act of 1931 are continued. According to Clause 40, the Pigs Marketing Board may itself set up Factories and cure, grade and sell bacon or, apparently, pigs that have not reached the bacon stage. What sort of disputes will have arisen or what sort of a mess will have been created before any future Board will try to make use of these powers, it is difficult to conjecture. We may be sure that there will have been sore trouble between the Farmers and the Curers before anything of the kind occurs.

The new proposals, like the old, except for this prospective action by the producers, are still limited to Bacon Pigs or to pigs more than sixteen weeks old—and the comments already made on this exclusion of all Pork Pigs remain unaffected.

It remains to be proved that any subsidy is required for bacon production, but if a case were made for special assistance in maintaining a proper level of price, bacon presents a case that would be easy to work, and I will use it as an example when discussing the workings of a levy-subsidy in the next chapter in connection with Import questions.

Eggs and Poultry

In the case of eggs the public is so willing to pay extra for good fresh eggs, and the discrepancy between spring and autumn prices is so wide, that the Commission would certainly proceed in the first place to promote a Producers'

[1] Clause 6, p. 7, lines 28–30.

Organisation that would be able to iron out these differences and produce a sensible average level for the producer, probably on the lines of the proposals already explained in Chapter XI, pp. 136–142.

It appears that the National Farmers' Union, and those promoting the modified scheme now being considered, are more anxious to have a case for increasing the duties on foreign eggs than for bringing about the vitally necessary changes in our own internal marketing arrangements. Under the Agricultural Marketing Act of 1933 a scheme for improved marketing at home is properly required as a condition antecedent to special assistance, and it is to be hoped that the authorities will look very carefully at any scheme that is more window dressing than reality before they accord any favours with regard to imports.

The two main facts in this connection are, first, that the people, especially children, require to eat a great many more eggs than they do, and second, that the public is prepared to pay a good price for reliable new-laid eggs and much prefers them to any others if they can get them. The suggestion, therefore, that the salvation of the poultry industry lies in putting higher taxes on imported eggs or in reducing the quantities imported, is a lazy way of shirking the necessities of the case at the expense of the community. A great to-do is made about "Chinese" eggs, but the fact is they are nearly all used in confectionery and manufacturing processes and do not enter into competition with fresh eggs at all. On the other hand, the evidence is overwhelming that there is an immensely increased market capable of being developed for fresh home-produced eggs, and they can readily be sold at materially higher prices than imported eggs. But we shall never get the prosperous condition that could be attained in our home market until there is capable management of egg marketing on a national scale as well as up-to-date arrangements for promoting increased consumption.

What applies to the sale of eggs, applies with equal force to the supply or the sale of Poultry through "service stations" operated on behalf of the Producers.

If the Poultry (Stock Improvement) Commission that
has been proposed by the Technical Committee whose
Report was referred to in Chapter XI, comes into existence,
it will provide an excellent instrument for assisting the
industry to obtain reliable stock and suffer less from
disease in consequence. If vested interests are able to
prevent the creation of such a body in the meantime, it
would be the duty of the National Agricultural Commission
we are considering to bring it into existence.

Potatoes

The Potato industry and the Potato Board provide a
welcome contrast to the incompetency that has characterised
dealing with bacon questions. Here again, however, nutritional guidance tells us that increased consumption is required
and the experiments that have already been made by the
assistance of the Board for the provision of cheaper potatoes
under simplified distribution arrangements in the Bishop-
Auckland district and elsewhere, give us a glimpse of the
possibilities that may be developed. It would be the business
of the Commission to check any attempts to inflate prices by
restricting acreage and to take in hand the promotion of
simpler and more economical distribution arrangements.

Market-Garden Produce

In this expression, for the present, we must include
green vegetables, tomatoes and glasshouse produce, as
well as fruit and flowers. It will be necessary to return to
the subject when dealing with the possibilities of future
development, but so far as the existing marketing arrangements are concerned—except as they have been improved
by better grading and packing of supplies under the National
Mark—they are a disgraceful mess. There is no such thing
as "a price". The Producer has to take what he can
get, and what he gets, apart from such examples as the
Cabbages and the Pershore plums already quoted, is often
less than a quarter of what the consumer pays.

The fault for all this is by no means to be attributed

to the greengrocer. He would probably be glad enough to trade on a smaller margin if he had a better and more reliable supply system. In this connection let me recall an experience I myself had some years ago. In the course of conversation with a greengrocer I was pointing out the discrepancy between the producer's and the consumer's price. Thereupon he asked me to come into his back premises. He pointed to a heap of earth and odds-and-ends of damaged potatoes which he had that morning sorted out from a sack that had come in. He said to me, with justice: "It's all very well, Doctor, to talk, but I was buying the man's potatoes, not his freehold!"

The incident shows clearly enough that the line of advance must be in the organised marketing on a graded basis of market-garden produce. There are National Mark schemes for a large number of supplies at present, with provision for the standardised grading and packing required, and many up-to-date growers use them, but this is a branch of production in which the small producer is prominent and the number of authorised packers is relatively small. It is obvious that there can be no satisfactory price standardisation unless it can be applied to a standardised product, and this means that improved organisation and price arrangements must go hand in hand.

A composite Producers' Board gradually extending the range of its activities over all the main items of market-garden produce is the first step. The very character, however, of much of the produce and the need for freshness indicates that there must be a regional system of economical assembly and transport based upon the chief consuming centres. In the case of these supplies, as in others, wholesalers would welcome arrangements that would provide them with a steady stream of properly graded supplies, and, although the undertaking is difficult, it presents no special difficulties except that it necessarily deals with a very diverse assortment of supplies.

One thing is specially important with regard to fruit —that is, the provision of facilities for modern gas or cold storage. The work at the East Malling Research Station and of the Food Preservation Research Department has shown what can be done in the keeping of apples in splendid condition for the greater part of the year. If good gas storage were available, there is no reason why we should not have Cox's Orange Pippins in excellent condition as late as Easter, or Bramley's Seedlings until July.

If the bulk of the supplies passing through the store is big enough, gas storage is an economical, indeed a highly remunerative proposition to the grower; but it needs to be on a big enough scale. A store of the capacity of 50 tons is said to be an economical unit for many varieties, although for some, such as Cox's, a smaller capacity will suffice. Such a scale of storage is beyond the means of small growers, and an early duty of a Marketing Board would be the liberal provision of storage facilities in different districts. Such regional Stores would also provide the means for co-operative sales on behalf of producers just as packing-stations will do for eggs. The producer would receive credit for the amount sent in to store, and, if necessary, a payment on account. Later on, sales would be made regularly as the market required and the producer would receive the balance of what was due to him, less the prescribed costs of storage and sale.

An early duty of the Commission, therefore, would be to set about the preparation of plans for the assistance of producers of market garden-supplies and for the promotion of the necessary machinery. Improved price arrangements would proceed hand in hand with them.

Producers' Requirements

There are two groups of producers' requirements which bulk largely in the costs of production: Fertilisers and Feeding-stuffs.

Unfortunately, in the case of Fertilisers the expenditure has been woefully deficient simply because the farmer has been short of cash and has purchased insufficient amounts, or gone without altogether. To some extent also, the small expenditure on fertilisers has been due to an imperfect appreciation of their value, but on the whole I should say that a deficiency of cash has been the more potent of the two. But whatever may have been the relative influence of these two reasons, the fact is that an immensely increased expenditure on fertilisers is required on a very great proportion of the land, and the large-scale purchase of them on behalf of farmers offers a ready opportunity for substantial help.

The rise in the cost of Feeding-stuffs during the past year has been a heavy handicap to poultry farmers and to the profitable feeding of pigs and live stock. To what extent these increases are fully warranted on the increased world prices of wheat, maize, barley and other ingredients, I cannot say. Certainly some of the big milling combines are making handsome profits. It is, however, certain that large reductions are obtainable (10s. a ton or more) on the usual market prices if purchases are made on a large scale.

Increases of cost during the past twelve months or so are about 2s. 6d. per cwt. to ordinary buyers. According to the Lane Fox Report the food-cost for a weaner pig, at 7s. 6d. per cwt. for food, is about 15s. From that stage to the bacon-pig stage the animal consumes seven cwts., thirty-five lbs., on the average, for a healthy pig. Thus the increase in food costs during the past year represents an added cost for each pig of about £1 2s. 4d.

There is certainly a field here in which a National Commission in concert with Home Commodity Boards could render great assistance to producers. We can scarcely expect that the Commission would decide to establish its own Milling and Manufacturing Corporations. We have to take the world as it is; and the method of approach would probably be in the form of agreements with existing Milling Corporations. The same, no doubt, would be the case with the great suppliers of fertilisers like the Imperial Chemical Corporation. These businesses are under enlightened and progressive direction and there is no reason to think that it would be difficult to negotiate arrangements which would be welcome to the Corporations themselves and a great advantage to the Producer.

PART II

SECTION VIII

Chapter XIV

Importation, Distribution and Wages

Importation Problems—Butter and Cheese—The Wheat Scheme—Levy-subsidies—Butter and Bacon—The Latest Bacon Scheme—*Distribution Problems*—Bread and Milk—*Wages*—The Labourer must benefit as a partner—A National Minimum Wage—A Rising Standard—Wage Machinery.

Importation

So FAR WE have been considering the Price Management and Marketing Duties of the National Commission as they relate to what can be done for home-produced supplies without special relation to the corresponding imports.

There is little or no competitive importation problem in the cases of liquid milk, potatoes and market-garden produce of many kinds. In regard to Eggs and Poultry the evidence before the Reorganisation Commission showed that imports competition was not very serious in view of the manifest advantages of fresh eggs and the public preference for them, whilst there was urgent need of sound internal management and a great possibility of the expansion of the demand for home supplies at fair prices if the case were efficiently dealt with.

The most remarkable case of the disproportionate importation of important articles of food which we are competent to produce in large quantities at home, are those of Butter and Cheese. The relative values of Home-produced and Imported supplies, according to estimates by the Ministry of Agriculture and the Milk Marketing Board, were as follows:—

OCTOBER 1935—SEPTEMBER 1936

	VALUE OF HOME-PRODUCED £	VALUE OF IMPORTED £
Butter		
Farmhouse —estimated	1,500,000	
Manufactured	3,437,000	
	4,937,000	44,026,720
Cheese	2,931,900	7,156,807
All other manufactured Milk Products	3,740,700	1,155,187

This case will call for examination in connection with Levy Subsidies together with that of Bacon, but before reaching that point we ought to face the general question of the case for Subsidies in any form, apart from any advantage that could be derived from improved internal organisation.

In that connection, and without prejudice to our subsequent examination of the case for the increased production of cereals in land development, reference should be made to the procedure now being adopted to give home-producers a stabilised price for wheat.

Subsidies—The Wheat Scheme

Under the Wheat Act of 1932 a levy is made on flour, either imported or milled, from home-produced or imported wheat, to such an amount as will enable the home grower to receive 10s. per cwt. (45s. per quarter) for the first 27,000,000 cwts. of home-grown wheat. This represents 6,000,000 quarters, or the product (at four quarters to the acre) of about 1,500,000 acres of wheat. The Act of 1937 increased the permissible quantity of home-grown wheat to 36,000,000 cwts., or to the product (at four quarters to the acre) of about 2,000,000 acres.

The amount that is charged per cwt. of flour is the difference between the average world-price for the year and 10s. per cwt.; so that the higher the world price the less is the "deficiency payment" into the Central Fund. In addition to this, if the wheat produced at home exceeds the prescribed quantity available for the subsidy, the amount paid per cwt. is scaled down accordingly. Thus, when wheat was a little over 4s. 7d. per cwt. in 1933–4, and 29,000,000 cwts were produced at home, the deficiency payment was 4s. 10d. per cwt., making an average return to the home-grower of 9s. 5d. But when, as in 1936–7, the average world price was 8s. 2d. per cwt. and the home output was only 26,000,000, the deficiency payment was 1s. 10d. to make up the full 10s. In this way a known scheme of price is provided, and if the home-grower produces in excess of the amount allowed for subsidy, the average price paid to him falls accordingly. If the world price reaches the limit of the guaranteed price, the subsidy ceases. The method has this advantage: as the amount of imported supplies exceeds the home production, the amount to be charged on each cwt. of imported supply falls accordingly and the average price at which flour can be released to the market is correspondingly reduced.

With this example before us let us return to the statement of principle that was put forward in the first chapter of this book. It is of vital importance. It was to the effect that in a self-respecting state of Society the people ought to have wages or income enough to pay such a price for their food as will ensure that the producer of it has as good a life as the rest of us. For my part I should refuse to describe such a payment to the Producer as a subsidy even if it were arbitrarily arranged for. The man who produces boots or coals is entitled to expect that he will obtain a good living out of the price of the boots or coals *because* he produces them, and the same should apply to the producer of corn, beef or butter.

If we depart from this principle see what a mess we shall soon be landed in!

At the present time, subsidies, hopefully intended for the producer, are being voted annually for beef, sugar, special milk supplies and others, to the extent of £14 million a year. They are defended sometimes by good friends of mine, on the ground that the subsidies are paid, in the main, by the better-to-do taxpayers and accordingly relieve the burden upon the multitude of consumers who are less well off. So far as that is concerned, it is true enough, but why should we stop at beef and sugar? Why not subsidise, through the taxpayer, coal, clothing and many more as well as bacon, butter or cheese? After all, coal, lighting and clothes are big items in the average worker's weekly budget. For my part I can see no reason whatever why, if it is right to subsidise the payment for a joint of beef from the taxpayer, it is not equally right to help him to pay for his coals. There is just as good a case for one as for the other—always provided, of course, that we make arrangements to secure that those for whom the benefit is intended really do get it—a thing that is not done at present.

If we are to proceed along these lines there would seem to be only one limit to it, that is until the taxpayer turns round and refuses to go on with it. It is as certain as anything can be that if this method of bolstering up the payment for necessities is to be adopted, sooner or later the taxpayer will revolt and insist upon a clean sweep being made of the whole business. Besides it is the entrenchment and fortification of poverty. People *ought not* to be so poor that they need to be subsidised in the weekly payment for the necessities of life. It is relief in kind on a national scale instead of on a parish scale. That is all.

The conclusion, as it seems to me, is that the only self-respecting procedure, and one that people will tolerate permanently, is to have a price system under which the price paid by the consumer contains, within itself, an adequate remuneration for those who have provided the goods for him and under which the Consumer himself has an income that enables him to pay it.

MA

For these reasons I suggest that the principle embodied in the payment for wheat is on sounder lines than general subsidies, although the nominal figure of 45s. per quarter is undoubtedly higher than efficient husbandry requires, and although the scheme should be accompanied by the control of market margins and of bread prices as well as by a self-respecting wage system. But the principle that, in the bread we buy, we pay a fair price to the home producer of wheat is surely right.

In the case of wheat, the system is based upon the necessity of keeping land under the plough, for important reasons that will be dealt with later on, as well as in order to provide an escape from the periodic slumps in price, which from time to time have made the cultivation of the crop financially impossible except on a basis of sweated wages.

The alternate slumps and booms in wheat prices, in the absence of any steady control of currency and prices, have been due to the fact that speculative operations, reinforced by the arbitrary operations of pools (which one year have been strong and another have collapsed) have operated without restraint in an entirely unorganised market. In addition to this there was large-scale production on virginal lands in the United States and Canada until the soil became exhausted, so that it was impossible to produce wheat in this country at an equally low cost. The United States has now practically ceased to be an exporter of wheat and the reckless use of much of the Canadian wheat land has already had its bitter consequences.

These erratic prices, however, only make more manifest the need for an orderly management of supplies and prices. Moreover, such management should be secured before we are entitled to say that other forms of price assistance should form a permanent part of our operations.

Levy-Subsidies

At the present time, wheat presents an extreme example of what may be described as a "levy subsidy", a system under which a certain charge is placed upon the imported product for the benefit of the home-producer, before it is liberated on to the market. In this case, as in any other that would be instituted, the charges are paid into a pool out of which the home-grower is paid the fixed or stabilised price. The nearer the price of the outside supplies approaches the stabilised price, the less is paid into the pool.

There are two major commodities in which a case might be made for a levy-subsidy under the system which the Commission would establish through the combined operations of the appropriate Home and Import Boards. They are Butter and Bacon. In either case the operation of such a system for the consumer would be infinitely less onerous than the results of a tariff, and might possibly be accompanied by market economies that would prevent any increase of retail price at all. It may be useful to consider how such a system could be worked with these two supplies.

Butter

The figures of quantities supplied by the Milk Marketing Board[1] show that in the year, October 1935 to September 1936, the butter produced and marketed in the United Kingdom was the equivalent of a little less than 147 million gallons of milk, whilst the butter imported into this country represented the product of little more than 2,500 million gallons, or rather more than sixteen times the amount of the home production. We should, however, make allowance for butter produced on farms apart from the factories. When this is taken account of, the imported supplies are about eleven times the home production.

The importation in 1936 from Empire and Foreign sources was as follows:—

	cwts.
Empire Supplies	5,137,025
Foreign Supplies	4,615,018

Empire butter is duty free, and 15s. per cwt. is charged on Foreign butter. On this basis the amount collected on Foreign butter was about £3,300,000 or equivalent to

[1] See Chapter XIII, p. 160.

an increased price to the consumer of a little more than
$1\frac{1}{2}d$. per lb. This tax, as present conditions show, does not
mean that the home producer of milk for butter receives
an adequate price. With infinite struggle the milk supplied
for that purpose (146 million gallons) has been increased
by a fraction of a penny up to $5\frac{1}{2}d$. or so. If it were
decided to increase the price paid for this milk by, say, $2d$.
per gallon, the cost would be about £1,250,000 per annum.

A levy on imported foreign butter of $\frac{3}{4}d$. per lb. would
produce £1,600,000. If a levy of this amount were repaid into
a pool from which the Milk Board would pay the additional
$2d$. per gallon to producers, it would more than cover the
amount required and leave a substantial margin against
reduction in foreign supplies or for increase in home supplies.

It would be the business of the National Commission,
first, to see that butter supplies were abundant, and,
second, to promote economics in distribution between the
Dock and the Shop counter to save as much of this $\frac{3}{4}d$.
per lb. as possible, which would be the only charge levied
on the foreign butter. The Commission would eliminate
uncertainty all along the line and would at least be able
materially to reduce the three farthings.

Thus the consumer would get the butter at a lower
price than he has to pay under the present duties, and
the home producer of milk for butter manufacture would
get a better price for his milk.

As a matter of arithmetic it is much cheaper than the
tariff method and has the merit of providing without
dubiety the advantage aimed at for the home producer.

Bacon

The case of bacon is equally interesting from this point
of view. When Mr. Elliot, in November 1932, sought to
provide for the home producer an extra price of $18d$.
per 20 lbs. by arranging for a 15 per cent restriction of
imports, at that time the Imports of Bacon were nearly
four times the home production of the corresponding
article. There were, however, further cuts in Imports

during the year until compulsory restrictions came into force in November 1933. Over the whole year the imports of Bacon were about three times the corresponding home production. Various price fluctuations occurred, but at the end of twelve months the results in wholesale and retail prices were as follows:—

	BRITISH WILTSHIRE GREEN	DANISH NO. 1
	Per cwt.	Per cwt.
	s. d.	s. d.
November 1932	75 0	57 0
November 1933	86 6	77 0

Retail Prices of streaky Bacon per lb.:—

	s. d.	s. d.
November 1932	$10\frac{1}{4}$	
November 1933	1 $0\frac{3}{4}$	

The wholesale price of British bacon thus increased by about 1d. per lb. and the retail 2½d. whilst the increase in price of Danish nearly corresponded to the increase in the retail price. In this way the British Producer got his extra 1d. per lb. whilst the consumer paid an extra 2½d.

During the year total supplies were diminished, and consumption fell because of the increase in the retail price. If instead of adopting this method of restriction and trusting to luck for its effect on home-producers' prices, an Import Board had been instructed to bring in all the supplies the market needed at as advantageous a price as it could, and pay into a pool a third of a penny per lb. on imported bacon (which was three times the amount of the home-produced supplies), the Pool would have been supplied with a Fund whereby the Home Producer could have been provided with his extra 1d. per lb. The payments would have been made through the Bacon Factories as an addition to the market price, much as is done in the case of wheat.

It would then have been the business of the Commission to introduce such economies and such added certainty into distribution and prices as would have saved the third of a penny per lb. between the Dock and the Counter. In any case even if the whole third of a penny had been added to the price of bacon in the form of, say, $\frac{1}{2}d$. per lb. it would have been only a fifth of the increase of price which actually followed.

As I have said already, a strong case would require to be made before even a system of this kind should be adopted, but as a mere matter of arithmetic it is immensely cheaper to the consumer than any tariff could be. It provides a standing incentive to producing economies in marketing and does secure that in what we buy we pay a living wage to the producer with no waste.

The overwhelming superiority of the method of National Control of the whole machinery here recommended is revealed in the shocking increases of retail prices that have taken place since 1933 under the irrational arrangements that were commented on in the previous chapter. The Producer is little better off than he was in November 1932; retail prices have risen 5d. per lb. with serious hardship to millions of consumers who cannot afford to buy the food they need.

Distribution

Now let us examine some of the possibilities that would be open to the National Commission, through its appropriate Commodity Boards, with regard to Distribution. By way of illustration it will suffice if we take the cases of Bread and Milk.

Bread

The expenditure of the average working-class family on Bread is higher than it would be if they were able to buy sufficient protective foods—eggs, milk, green vegetables, etc. But putting that aside for the present, the Royal Commission on Food Prices,[1] already referred to, showed that the average expenditure per family for bread

[1] Royal Commission on Food Prices, 1925.

each week was one-fifth of their total expenditure on food and that an increase of a 1d. in the price of a quartern loaf represented, in the aggregate, an increased food bill of £10,000,000 per annum. It is very discreditable to us that no effective steps have yet been taken to promote the economies in bread distribution which the Royal Commission found to be urgently required. It is true that in consequence of the state of affairs then revealed a Food Council was appointed. But it was not given any powers. It can only make enquiries and report to the President of the Board of Trade.

Within the narrow limits prescribed for it, the Food Council has rendered conspicuous service and its Reports are able and independent documents, but each succeeding report only testifies the more strongly to its pathetic helplessness. The Bakery Trade has continued to go its own way with conspicuous success despite the Council.

So far as one can find from the Reports of the Council, including the most recent,[1] the disorders that the Royal Commission so forcibly pointed out continue unabated. The Commission found that the profits usually made on the bread obtained from a standard sack of flour exceeded the labour production costs; that "the figures supplied by the National Association of Master Bakers need to be modified because they minimise output and in certain respects magnify costs".[2]

They found also that the local Associations fixed prices on the basis of satisfying all concerned—including the least efficient—and that, therefore, "all members of the trade being satisfied, the price of the article will remain at a higher level than if prices are fixed by competition and not by arrangement".[3] No wonder, therefore, that the same paragraph concluded, "we are therefore of opinion that the system of price-fixing requires close investigation and continued supervision by a permanent and impartial body, and that these duties should be placed on the Food Council".

The Food Council was given authority to "investigate" but no powers whatever for "continuous supervision",

---

[1] Report for 1936.   [2] *Ibid.* Par. 85, p. 37.   [3] *Ibid.* Par. 68, p. 28.

and it is perfectly evident from the tenor of their successive reports that the finding of the Royal Commission is still warranted. That finding, after discussing retail profits,[1] was in the following terms:—

"We consider that retail profits of this size are too high as a general average and that the *retail price of bread should be reduced*, not uniformly over the whole country, but by substantial adjustments in certain areas."

It appears also that the practice, so closely investigated and so strongly condemned by the Royal Commission, of with-holding supplies of flour from bakers who wish to reduce retail prices, still continues where it can be managed. The last report of the Food Council plaintively testifies to their helplessness in the matter. They call attention to it again[2] and recall that it has been condemned both by the Linlithgow Committee and the Royal Commission, and add:—

"We recommended (in a previous Report) that such a weapon should never be used except possibly against a baker who was selling bread at an uneconomic price, and that provision should be made in such cases for appeal to an independent tribunal."

There is no such Tribunal; nor is there likely to be under the present dispensation.

The long and short of it is that, in the case of Bread —which has been the subject of "Reports" for a period of nearly fourteen years—there is an unchallengeable case for such a Body as the National Commission we are considering, with adequate powers over marketing arrangements and Distribution Margins.

In another respect the case is getting worse. It was contended before the Royal Commission that only 92·4 quartern loaves were obtained, on the average, from a standard sack of flour. But a test at Aldershot revealed that 95 loaves were obtained and that, by hand-baking,

[1] Report for 1936. Par. 104, p. 44. (My italics.)   [2] *Ibid.* p. 8.

at Shorncliffe, 96½ were obtained. Since that time, how-ever, "scientific" baking has made great advances, and I am informed that from 100 to 102 quartern loaves can now be obtained by up-to-date methods from the same weight of flour. In other words it has become possible to sell some 24 lbs. additional weight of bread from the same sack of flour. What is that additional weight? It is water. The flour, by "scientific" methods is made to absorb 24 lbs. additional weight of water. No wonder, when I was discussing this problem with an important deputation in 1931, one of the prominent members exclaimed: "The problem of the scientific baker is to make water stand up!" But the public is not paying proportionately less per quartern loaf.

With the efficient millers' organisations that now exist and with the assistance of the Co-operative Societies, it would certainly be practicable, under the authority of the National Commission, to establish workable margins that would be incentives to economy and give the con-sumer the benefit.

Remember all the time that a halfpenny per quartern loaf saved is £5,000,000 per annum off the National Bread Bill.

Milk

In this connection, and to an extent which I hope will not bore the reader, I must return once more to the subject of milk. The case is so glaring and has been made so often that there is no need to re-state it, but it is evident that the way—and indeed the only way—to secure the necessary economies is to bring the whole of milk dis-tribution under the control of a Central authority. It does not seem to matter much what Commission, Council or Committee examines this subject, the conclusions, in essentials, are always the same. An enormous increase of consumption is required in the interests of health, and one of the biggest obstacles to that increase is the high retail price.

In their Report for 1936 the Food Council tells us that the results of expert investigation showed that "the desirable amount of milk for children was from one to two pints per day, and about two pints for expectant and nursing mothers",[1] whilst numerous reports show that the actual consumption in poorer paid workers' families is an eighth of a pint and often none at all, and that the average for the whole population is only about a third of a pint per day.

At the same time we are told that "the retail price of milk as recorded by the Ministry of Labour stands higher in relation to pre-war than that of any other food except fish".[2]

The explanation for all this is set out fully in the Report of the Second Reorganisation Commission for Milk published in November 1936 and was confirmed in detail by a further examination of the "Costs and Profits of Retail Milk Distribution" published by the Food Council late in 1937.

The present price-fixing arrangements of the Distributors' Associations make it impossible for those who are both able and willing to sell milk at lower prices, to do so; and there is an unassailable case for what has so often been contended here, namely, that Price-fixing in its final form should be taken out of the hands of the Producers' Boards and made the responsibility of an independent Central Authority.

At the same time the Reports show clearly enough that the present high retail prices are due to a needless multiplicity of distributors, each of them often distributing trivial amounts of milk daily; to deliveries twice a day, even in half pints, when one delivery should suffice, and to the cultivation of a public expectation of all sorts of services that are necessarily costly and often quite uncalled for.

Alongside this, milk prices are raised higher than they need be because they are now being used to subsidise milk at low price for manufacture. We therefore have the spectacle of milk being supplied for making chocolate and many other things besides butter, at $5\frac{1}{2}d.$ a gallon, whilst people have to pay more than five times as much for milk to drink.

[1] Report for 1936. p. 13. [2] Loc. cit., p. 14.

The Reorganisation Commission recommended that a Central Authority should have authority to plan a production policy which would involve placing the manufacturing side upon a separate basis, to fix prices and to frame measures for the stimulation of the consumption of milk. This means that the Central Authority (or National Milk Authority) would have power to promote a rational and economical system of distribution.

It would no doubt arrange for the creation of regional, or local, milk distribution organisations with adequate arrangements for collection, cleaning, bottling and distribution. In many places this would only mean the grafting of extended duties and responsibilities on to what exists already.

If we had a clear field, I confess I should like to see it made a duty of the Municipal Authorities, but we have to take things as they are, and we may anticipate that the scheme would provide for the use of existing agencies, where they are efficient, and for their appropriate amalgamation. The Co-operative Societies in a great many places are outstanding in their efficiency, and in other districts the organisations of well-managed concerns like the United Dairies and others are obviously those that would be incorporated in a National Scheme.

It would, I think, be an easy matter to find a Body of men on the Co-operative movement and in other well-managed private concerns who would administer a national milk distribution scheme for us with outstanding efficiency, as well as with goodwill. The development would probably take the form of a Milk Distribution Corporation working on lines approved by the National Commission.

We should have to be prepared to pay compensation for the extinction of existing goodwill in some cases, although, as a matter of fact, many of the smaller existing distributors now derive their supplies from the larger concerns. Whatever this might amount to, it would soon be extinguished in the economies that were attainable.

We should then be on the high road to the increased milk consumption that is so urgently necessary and be possessed of a National Authority whose aim and credit would depend upon producing economies and encouraging consumption.

Wages and the Labourer

So far, when Producers' Prices have been spoken of, we have been considering the operations of the National Commission from the point of view of the average Producers prices. The Agricultural Labourer, however, is just as much a Producer as the Farmer or Manager, although he is not, as such, a party to sales transaction. Unless, therefore, we take care that, *of necessity*, he is a participant in the benefits of improved price arrangements, we incur the risk of the benefits being taken by the individual farmers or by the agricultural corporations that may come into being.

We must, therefore, secure as an *essential concomitant* of the plan, that better wages are automatically promoted as a part of its development.

Whatever form land cultivation may take, it will depend largely upon the employment of labour paid weekly wages, even if those wages may be supplemented by some form of co-operative sharing in the profits of the enterprise. The employment of more men under good and attractive conditions upon the land is inseparable from the increased production of food and better cultivation of the land. Humanly speaking, it really takes the first place.

The standard to be aimed at must be that conditions of life on the land—including in that expression, wages, housing, and opportunities for social intercourse and a happy life—are at least as good and attractive in the village as they are in the town.

It is unfortunately not to be expected, in view of the big gap that exists at present, that we shall get there all at once, but it ought to be a condition of the scheme that it is progressively attained.

For these reasons there ought to be a *National Minimum Standard* of wage, and that standard should increase annually for a given term of years as development proceeds.

If the agricultural worker knew that each year, say, for the next ten years, his minimum standard of wage would rise annually he would have something to look forward to.

In any case it must be insisted that *from the beginning* the minimum standard is substantially higher than the present average rate of wages, and the price system should be adjusted to take that into account. The average County standard at present throughout the country is about 34s. per week. In some counties it is as high as 39s.; in others as low as 32s. 6d.

We ought to bring the minimum up to £2 per week at least at the start; and I believe that this could be attained.

In making the suggestion that the minimum should be fixed at the start at a modest £2 a week, although it is a figure far below what good industrial workers receive, I am well aware that it will be received by a good many with protests that it is quite impossible, and "will ruin agriculture". I do not believe it.

The labour costs of production in agriculture, as with many industries, when the costs are carefully and scientifically apportioned, will be found to be greatly less than many people suppose. This statement is supported by many well-kept farm accounts. The production per man, since 1921, as already stated, has increased 40 per cent in value—largely due, no doubt, to the introduction and use of machinery—and we must have a system whereby the labourer himself receives a full share of the benefits of his own productivity.

If, say, the immediate rise in wages represented 5s. a week per man, or £13 per annum, it would still, for the whole 600,000 agricultural labourers regularly employed, be not much more than half of what has already been granted in the way of subsidies. Moreover, when we take account of the smaller number employed, it appears that, notwithstanding recent increases in wages, the total paid in wages has diminished by at least £1,000,000 a year since 1923.

If the increased assistance that would be given under the national system we are contemplating in terms of improved equipment and fair prices is not worth much more than half the present subsidies, then the system will be a failure. As Sir Daniel Hall said in a moving phrase in that splendid little book of his on "Agriculture After the War":[1] "If we are to believe that agriculture is outside the scope of British intelligence and organisation, the sooner we put up the National shutters, the better." Farming is just as susceptible of exact knowledge and sound business treatment as any other industry, and we must refuse to believe that we cannot make British agriculture as well able to provide a good and attractive living for its workers as any other industry.

There is no reason why a *minimum* wage should become the *standard* wage. It is not so amongst the Counties. The conditions of the industry are so various and the types of employment so different that County Committees everywhere make provision for higher rates than the County standard for some classes of workers, and these adjustments would certainly continue.

How would these arrangements be provided for?

The National Wages Board would have to be reconstituted on similar lines, and with similar powers, to those possessed by the Board that was wrecked after the war. It would have the final determination of the National minima of wages and working conditions. It would be advised and assisted by the County Committees, but they would have no final authority except so far as they were authorised to deal with special rates or conditions peculiar to their area.

The National Agricultural Commission would prescribe the number of years during which the minimum would automatically rise and would plan its production and price policy with this important consideration before it all the time.

[1] *Agriculture after the War*, Sir Daniel Hall, John Murray 1920, 3rd edition, p. 51.

PART III

A PROGRAMME
OF DEVELOPMENT

PART III

SECTION I

Chapter XV

Some Special Needs

Needs, a Guide to Development—Outstanding Food Needs—A Report by Scientists—The Increased Production of Protective Foods in Relation to Present Production—The Increase Required in Milk and Milk Products, Eggs, Fruit, Vegetables and Meat—War-Time Needs—Usual Stocks—Animal Feeding-stuffs—Storage—What is Most Required—How these Affect a Programme—Neglected Timber Production.

So FAR, IN Part I (Chapters II to VI), I have reviewed the present state of affairs on the land, the conditions of life of those who work upon it, and the reasons for the continued decline in Agriculture. In Part II (Chapters VII to XIV) I have dealt with the important changes that are necessary and with the means whereby restoration might be effected and prosperity brought back to the countryside if the Nation is prepared to adopt them. It now remains to consider a programme of development that might be contemplated in the light of existing knowledge.

It needs little experience in public affairs to forecast the kind of opposition which the machinery that has been suggested would meet with. There would be a number of powerful Boards. There would be a Central Authority with great powers. There would be County Committees of an important character, and the upholder of the present muddle and drift will cry aloud about "hordes of officials" and seek to confuse the public mind, and thus perpetuate the present drift with all its thousands of agencies, dealers, jobbers and the rest who batten in the sacred name of private enterprise upon producer and consumer alike.

This sort of criticism has got to be faced up to, as it readily can be. The proper reply is to make a comparison between the trivial costs of the big-scale

Na

National organisations that were given an account of in Chapter XII, (as well, for instance, of those of the present Milk Board, whose total administrative expenses amount to about one-tenth of a penny per gallon) and the multitude of tolls that are levied upon the Producer by the existing marketing system as already displayed.

Nevertheless the National ownership of the Land and the elaborate machinery designed to give security to the Producer and safeguards for the Consumer will only be justified by their results.

My task now is to set out the plan of development that present conditions show to be necessary and attainable. As time goes on, and as experience develops, the plan may well proceed far beyond what I shall forecast in this and succeeding Chapters, but we have enough to go on at present to justify a programme of development which, if it were carried through, would undoubtedly restore Agriculture, and provide accordingly a greatly added measure of national security.

The plan of development must take account, first, of outstanding Needs; second, of our Capacity to meet them —and, third, of the means whereby the plan may be given effect to.

Needs

Needs may be examined from two points of view: those which are prominent in the interest of ordinary agricultural development, and those which would emerge in time of war.

In the state of affairs that exists in the world today we are bound to take account of the situation that would be presented to us if we became involved in war with other major Powers. It is true that, if war did occur, it would be an expression of human insanity, but it is no use pretending that it may not occur; and although it might be folly in times of peace to make the exceptional uses of the land that the peril of famine might necessitate, we are bound to have those possibilities in mind when planning a scheme of development that will be justified in itself in times of peace.

Let us examine Needs from those two points of view.

Peace-Time Existing Needs

They are primarily the needs of the people for food. The subject has been referred to many times and it is now necessary to focus the requirements in terms of the increased production called for.

In this connexion I must refer to a Report which has not been made public as it ought to have been, but the contents of which, in substance, are well known to many, including myself.

In June 1934 as already mentioned[1] a number of Scientists made a Report to the Government upon the need for improved nutrition of the people. The signatories of the Report were of such exceptional authority that, party politics apart, their Report should have been made public. One cannot fairly say that, if it had been, it would have added much to existing knowledge, but it would have added an unchallenged authority to the account of widespread ill-nourishment that has been revealed by the enquiries of Sir John Orr and his friends, by the League of Nations Committee, and by many others. We go about our daily work and are so interested in current events that we lose sight of the shocking defects of nutritional origin from which the nation suffers. It is the more to be regretted because these defects are so largely removable if we would apply in national policy the recommendations that are made to us.

I have already made a general review of these deficiencies in Chapter VIII, but it will be useful here to refer in a little detail to the findings of the Scientists and then summarise the rest in order that they may be translated into an increased food production programme.

The chief facts found by the Scientists are these: In 1932, 52·1 per cent of the recruits examined for the army

[1] page 81 et seq.

were rejected on physical or medical grounds; that is, more than half of the young men, presumably in the prime of life, who presented themselves. Nearly three-quarters of those who were rejected were rejected on physical grounds alone; apart, from the ascertainment of any medical disability. It appears that 25 per cent of the children of the Professional classes are above the average standard of height, 70 per cent of them attain it and only 5 per cent of them are below it; whereas of the poorer classes of the community only 2 per cent are above the average height and 47 per cent are below it. We are told also that this smallness of stature is accompanied by a standard of health that is not so good as it should be. Various bone deformities resulting from rickets were commonly seen, as well as defects of the chest often associated with rickets, and many other defects of nutritional origin. In the case of women the defect of rickets is sometimes manifested in an insufficient growth in the pelvic bones so as to affect child-bearing, and the Scientists reported that rickets will undoubtedly continue to be a common disorder unless an organised policy of feeding is adopted. It has been shown also that the widespread defects in children's teeth are largely derived from a diet that is defective in essential ingredients. The same applies to the disorder of the mouth called pyorrhœa that so often accompanies bad teeth. Another nutritional disease of great importance is anaemia, particularly in children and pregnant and nursing women. Its existence is determined by a blood test and a sample investigation in Newcastle amongst poorer children showed 23 per cent of them to be anaemic and another enquiry in London amongst child-bearing women revealed that anaemia was common, that 45 per cent of their infants who were breast-fed, and 51 per cent of those artificially fed were found to be definitely anaemic.

It is not necessary to continue this recital in technical details, but it is established that there are two main defects in the average diet of a large section of the people; namely the over-consumption of cereals in the form of bread and similar foodstuffs, and under-consumption of certain foodstuffs that are called "Protective", particularly milk, butter, cheese, eggs, fruit and green vegetables. This does not mean that bread foods are not good foods, but it does mean that the diet of which they ought to form a part should contain these other foods in sufficient quantities, otherwise their diet is defective, as the Scientists tell us, in calcium, fat, soluble vitamins and first-class biological protein.

The value of milk has often been referred to, but it may be useful to epitomise the ascertained results of giving a pint of milk daily to children in addition to normal diet, and compare the results with those that did not receive it. The average growth in one year of those who received the milk was 2·63 inches as compared with 1·84 in those who continued their normal diet. The former children, also, added 6·98 lbs. to their weight during the year whilst the latter only added 3·85.

It is difficult sometimes for people to realise that some of the foods mentioned are so important. If for example the diet consisted, say, of bread, oatmeal, rice, sugar, margarine, lard, meat, poultry, fish and jam it would still be defective in some ingredients that are important in the formation of bone and teeth. This example only illustrates the enormous importance of keeping clearly in mind the value of the "protective" foods already mentioned. For instance, the diet of a woman during pregnancy and lactation should include a pint and a half of milk a day, one or two eggs or their yolks and a serving of green vegetables, and there should be some fish at least twice a week.

An infant after being weaned should have in its diet at least a pint of milk and one egg yolk daily. After it has become a year old, and up to twelve years of age, it ought to have, somewhere in its daily food, a pint and a half of milk as well as egg yolk and green vegetables, and the Scientists also tell us that the majority of adults would be in better health if they consumed regularly more milk, butter, cheese, eggs and vegetables as well as fruit. In addition to these "Protective Foods" some addition, they say, should be made to the Meat consumed.

There are 13,500,000 people whose average expenditure on food is 6s. a week or less. They represent the lowest two groups in Sir John Orr's analysis of the population in terms of their income; and the next group above them contains a further nine million persons whose ability to spend in food does not exceed 8s. a week.

The exhaustive enquiries that have been made show that the diet of the first two groups is seriously inadequate in nearly all respects. The higher of them, in Group 2, do get a sufficiency of protein and fats in quantity, but they are deficient in quality. One meat meal a week, and that often of poor quality, appears to represent the fare in this respect of a great proportion of people of these income classes.

Better-to-do people, as a rule, eat more meat than they need, and often suffer in consequence. But there should be a substantial increase in meat consumption in the lowest-paid sections of the population if their diet is to be adequately balanced.

Now let us convert this much-needed increased consumption of protective foods and of meat into terms of the increased production required.

Milk and Milk Products

The present production of milk in the United Kingdom for all purposes is 1,209,900,000 gallons.

Of this amount at present

773,400,000 gallons

go into liquid consumption. The increased consumption that would be called for if children and mothers, as well as others, were to have the milk they need, would represent an addition to the amount now consumed of nearly 50 per cent, say

350,000,000, gallons.

Even when this amount had been added, the average consumption in this country would still be less than it now is in the United States, Denmark, Norway, Switzerland or Holland.

This increase of milk for liquid consumption would absorb nearly the whole of the milk we now produce (436 million gallons) which goes into butter, cheese, and other products.

Butter and Cheese

When we come to Butter and Cheese we are presented with a task which is simply staggering in its dimensions. Converting the imported butter into terms of its equivalent gallonage of milk, it appears that it represents.

$$2,506,900,000 \text{ gallons of milk.}$$

The present home production of butter for the market in gallons of milk is only 146·9 million gallons !

Our total consumption of butter in terms of milk gallons therefore is

$$2,653,800,000$$

The minimum increase of butter that the people ought to consume is estimated at 25 per cent of our present consumption, or the equivalent of an additional

$$663,800,000 \text{ gallons of milk.}$$

The consumption of cheese, also, should be increased by a minimum of 25 per cent. The gallonage of milk represented in the cheese at present consumed is

$$411,900,000,$$

of which 124·6 million gallons are produced at home. If we allow for this increase of 25 per cent in the cheese consumption, it means the additional production of a little over

$$100,000,000, \text{ gallons of milk.}$$

These three together—liquid milk, butter and cheese— reveal an additional milk requirement as follows:—

For Liquid Milk	350,000,000 galls.
Liquid Milk for butter manufacture	663,800,000 ,,
Liquid Milk for cheese manufacture	100,000,000 ,,
Total	1,113,800,000 ,,

For all practical purposes, therefore, we conclude that the present milk production in this country would require to be nearly doubled if the extra butter and cheese were to be produced at home—apart entirely from producing any of the vast quantities of butter we now import.

Eggs

The consumption of eggs in the United Kingdom at the present time is about 160 eggs per head per annum. In many other countries the consumption is much larger. For example, in the United States and Canada the consumption formerly was about 260 eggs per person per annum, but under an effective system of grading it has risen to 360 eggs.[1]

Our own consumption of eggs in shell last year was

6,000,000,000

The home contribution to this total was

3,347,000,000

The minimum estimate which any of the nutritional experts have provided is that there should be an increased consumption of at least 25 per cent, although if this figure were reached we should still be far short of the standards of some other countries, the United States and Canada.

If we put the necessary increase at a third, we should still be consuming only 213 eggs per head per annum.

On this low basis egg consumption should be increased by about

2,000,000,000, eggs per annum,

that is, 33·3 per cent of our present consumption.

[1] Report of the Reorganisation Commission for Eggs and Poultry England and Wales, 1935, p. 12.

If this increase in egg consumption were to be derived from home production only, it would mean that our present output would require to be increased by about 60 per cent.

Fruit

The expression "Fruit" is a wide term and in ordinary domestic use overlaps into what are usually classed as vegetables, for instance, tomatoes. We may, however, safely exclude the more costly imported fruits, although we certainly should include oranges and lemons. At this place, however, we are considering our needs in terms of supplies that are produced at home.—Tomatoes will be taken with vegetables, as they are separately classified from Fruits in the official returns.

The expression "Fruit", therefore, in this connection applies to home-grown fruit, that is, to Apples, Pears, Plums, Cherries, Strawberries, Raspberries, Red, Black and White Currants and Gooseberries and a few other small supplies.

The present consumption of these fruits is

$$19,597,843 \text{ cwts.,}$$

of which a little over 12,500,000 cwts. are derived from home sources.

The minimum estimate which any experts have provided is that there should be an increased consumption both of fruit and of vegetables of 53 per cent.

There are certainly no better fruits grown in the world than the wholesome fruits mentioned in the above list, of which our home production of dessert and cooking apples provides rather more than half the total quantity. If we take an increased requirement of 50 per cent we are certainly well within the mark of what the people ought to consume on health account.

A 50 per cent increase on present consumption represents about

$$9,750,000 \text{ cwts. per annum.}$$

If this increased quantity were provided from home sources it would mean an increased production of 78 per cent.

Vegetables

I have unfortunately not been able to obtain a precise statement of the quantities of home-grown vegetables, but, from the returns available to them, the Ministry of Agriculture estimates that the present national consumption is

$$£30,435,000 \text{ in value.}$$

Of this amount £5,420,000 represents the value of imported onions and tomatoes, and the balance the estimated value of our existing market-garden produce together with the product of the cultivation of 1,726 acres of tomatoes.

[The total acreage now devoted to vegetable production at home and passing through markets, (apart from the amounts used in the households of the Producers) is 250,161 acres in England and Wales, to which should be added the product of about 50,000 acres in Scotland.]

The home production, therefore, of vegetables and tomatoes in value is about £25,000,000 per annum.

An increased consumption of vegetables is probably as necessary as any and if we allow for an increased requirement of 50 per cent we are well below the usual expert's statement of our need. This means that in terms of present value the consumption should be increased by £15,200,000 worth per annum.

If the whole of this were obtained by increased home production it would mean that it would require to be increased by 60 per cent.

Meat

As already explained in this analysis of increased food consumption required, we ought to take account of meat although it is not classified as a Protective Food.

The lowest estimate that I can find is that the extra meat consumption required for the lowest income classes of the population would be represented by about an increase of 12 per cent.

For these purposes it will suffice to make our reckoning in terms of beef, mutton and lamb and Pig Meat. The present total national consumption of these three together is something over 53,000,000 cwts. It will suffice if we take round figures and express beef and veal consumption as 25,000,000 cwts. per annum, mutton and lamb as 11,000,000 and Pig Meat as 17,000,000 cwts.

A 12 per cent increase of these supplies would be represented by an addition of more than 6,000,000 cwts.

The present contribution from home sources to our total consumption is:—

Beef and Veal	12,790,000 cwts.
Mutton and Lamb	4,849,000 ,,
Pig Meat	8,206,000 ,,

If the increased supplies that are required, therefore, were to be supplied at home, in the existing proportion of production, it would mean an increase of about 25 per cent in each or rather more. For present purposes, say, an addition of three million cwts. of beef, one million of mutton, and two million cwts. of Pig Meat.

If we bring together into a composite table the increased requirements of protective foods and of meat that have emerged from the foregoing review we are confronted with this result:—

	Increased Consumption Required.	*Increase on present production. If obtained from home sources.*
Milk (For liquid consumption, Butter and Cheese)		*per cent*
	1,113 million galls.	Nearly 100
Eggs	2,000 million	60

	Increased Consumption Required.	Increase on present production. If obtained from home sources.
		per cent
Fruit	9,750,000 cwts.	78
Vegetables	15,000,000 (£ value)	60
Beef, Mutton and Pig Meat	6,000,000 cwts.	25

Let me emphasise again, however, that the increase of home production so far referred to takes no account whatever of our producing, as we ought to do, a substantial part of the butter, eggs, fruit and meat that we now import.

War-Time Needs

We cannot plan the course of agriculture that should be developed in the ordinary life of the nation in terms of the emergencies that might confront us in war, but we must take account of them in so far as they affect the peace-time plan of production that ought to be followed.

If, for example, we had a safety storage system[1] as a part of our national practice it would affect the extent to which additional ploughing would require to be undertaken in the first year of a war, and the proportions in which meat production could wisely be continued.

In order that we may have war-time necessities in mind when we consider an enlarged extension programme, let me summarise in terms of food supplies the chief emergencies with which the nation would be confronted.

Our experiences in this respect are so near, and so closely related to the present condition of home agriculture, that many of the bitter lessons we learnt during the Great War are applicable today.

I may perhaps be permitted at this place to recall an unforgettable personal experience. In January 1917 I

[1] Since this was written some announcements of the Government's plans have been made. They appear to accord to a great extent with what is suggested.

became a member of a small Cabinet Committee whose duty it was to meet almost daily, and, in the light of the reports that came to us from the Ministry of Shipping, from the Admiralty, from the Ministry of Food, the Board of Trade and other Departments, to make recommendations to the Government for the curtailment of and apportionment of national supplies according to the urgency of the need represented to us. During the first four months of 1917 the sinking of ships by submarines increased daily to an alarming extent until a climax was reached one day in April 1917 when no less than thirty-four ships containing important supplies were sent to the bottom. More than once our reserves of sugar were only a few hours, and butter, lard and margarine were little better. The line which separated the nation from starvation was often perilously thin.

At the present time it would be nothing short of crazy if we failed to take some of the obvious and effective steps which emerge from the lesson of those terrible days.

A reference to the table of our chief food supplies in Chapter XIII, page 159, shows what proportion of them we produce at home, but it must be remembered that the production of some of them, wheat and sugar, for example, is seasonal in its character so that the stocks existing in the country are not in the same proportions all the year round. Apart from our own harvest, which provides a corn supply of about ten weeks, the stocks of wheat and flour in the country commonly provide for about six weeks. In the case of butter, in which we are so largely dependent upon imported supplies, the usual stocks provide about two weeks. The position with regard to other fats, particularly lard and margarine, is worse: the normal stocks provide only for a few days, a week at the most. In the case of sugar, the present home production, which has been developed entirely since the war, places us in a stronger position than we were then. If our home-produced supplies were spread out evenly throughout the year they would provide for nearly a third of our requirements.

This, however, would necessitate a great addition to present storage capacity because, as the sugar is refined, it passes quickly on to the .market. In the ordinary way the stocks of sugar otherwise are little more than a week's supply.

The imports of chilled and frozen beef, which form so large a proportion of our meat imports, are normally represented by stocks of about two weeks. Supplies of meat, however, in war-time could be supplemented by slaughter at home, but this would soon affect our meat-producing capacity, although it would diminish our dependence upon imported feeding-stuffs.

Eggs, whether imported or home-produced, pass very quickly on to the market, and for practical purposes stocks in reserve are practically nil. This, of course, would not be so if there were a proper provision for cold storage such as I indicated as desirable in the interest of the ordinary marketing of home-produced supplies.

Alongside these scanty stocks of vital foods it is to be remembered that our ability to produce some of them is largely dependent on the importation of different feeding-stuffs because of our small arable acreage. In 1935, for example, we imported nearly 13,000,000 cwts. of barley-meal and flour, rye-meal, bran, sharps and middlings, and other various meals mainly used for animal feeding. These, however, bulky as they were, were only a fifth of the quantity of maize that was imported, which amounted to 60,000,000 cwts. Maize is largely used in distilleries and, indirectly, yeast production depends upon the distilleries which use maize, but a large proportion of the maize is destined for animal feeding, so that our ability to continue to produce milk, butter, cheese and meat of all kinds, as well as eggs and poultry, is bound up with this immense volume of cereal importation. With the exception of maize we are capable of producing a large part of these feeding-stuffs, but, in the absence of storage, our dependence upon these supplies must be a determining factor in the cultivation policy to be pursued if the country were confronted with war in the present circumstances.

At the same time it adds great cogency to the case that I seek to establish later on, that (in the interests of the best use of the land itself as well as on account of the food production and employment it would give rise to) a bold programme of increase in the amount of arable cultivation is urgently required. The increase in the production of animal feeding-stuffs would be of first-rate importance in helping us to maintain our production of meat, milk, butter and eggs.

The circumstances just referred to limit our freedom to plan agricultural production upon lines best suited to the soil for peace-time development, because we are so shockingly short of facilities for storing sufficient quantities of those supplies that are capable of being stored for considerable periods in good condition.

Storage is affected by two main considerations: the suitability of the food in question for prolonged storage without deterioration, and the interchangeability of the shipping adopted for its transport. From this double point of view, so far as food storage is concerned, there is no doubt that sugar, wheat and flour, fats and oils, in that order, should be stored in large quantities. Sugar can be stored under proper conditions for a long time without damage, and the same applies to wheat if it is properly looked after. It appears that long-term, large-scale storage of flour is not at present so reliable as that of wheat. The storage of wheat also would present the immense advantage that it provides the animal feeding-stuffs that would be obtainable in the process of milling. The three main fats that should be stored in large quantities are butter, margarine and lard. They are very precious as foods and, fortunately, the tonnage they require is only about a fifth of that which is now devoted to maize.

The fate of our convoys of sugar and wheat during the last war, except for the last few months, was a subject of daily anxiety, and it so happens that ships adapted for their transport can readily be used for many other types of important cargoes.

It is not my business in this book to elaborate these matters in other directions, or to refer to other cargoes of which the transport was often very critical during the war. But there is no doubt that the existence of storage capable of accommodating a year's supply of wheat, sugar and the three main fats, would provide a safeguard for the nation, the importance of which cannot possibly be exaggerated.

For the purposes of the policy we are here considering such storage would enable us to plan land utilisation on much better lines than would otherwise be the case, because we should know that the adequate provision of these stores of human and animal food would give us the priceless advantage of having a whole season in hand to adapt our food-producing policy to war emergencies.

The cost of a year's storage of wheat has been variously estimated to cost from £2½ to £4 million. Even at the higher figure it is a trivial cost in insurance against the dangers we should be safeguarded from. I have not seen any reliable estimates as to the similar costs for the storage of sugar and fats, but they would be substantially less, as their volume is so much smaller.

It should be said in conclusion that the position today is much worse than it was in 1914, for two main reasons. The shipping tonnage available is less, and the dangers to convoys have been increased by the developments of wireless communications and the use of aircraft.

The review of needs which has formed the subject of this Chapter has purposely not taken account of that other great need which is the main theme of this book, namely the proper and adequate use of our splendid land and the employment under happy conditions of those who live upon it, as well as of that increased number that might be added to them.

The need of our land for a better use must be determined by its suitability and capacity, and that subject, over a wide range of products, will provide the theme for our next chapter before we pass on to consider how those capacities could best be developed. But this review of the foods which the people need in greatly increased quantities, as well as of the character of the dangers with which war would confront us, provide us with two important guides for policy. In the first place the protective foods, milk, butter, cheese, eggs, fruit and vegetables, are those which, by singular good fortune, we are exceptionally well able to produce. The first four of them (animal products) depend upon the supply of feeding-stuffs, as does the extra quantity of meat we require, and these animal feeding-stuffs, in turn, depend upon the use of the plough and the extent to which the productive capacity of our land can be increased by its use. It follows, therefore, that the increased use of the plough and of land cultivation according to modern methods, both for the production of human and animal food, provides the key to the increased production we ought to plan in order to enable us to reap the proper harvest of peace as well as to provide a safeguard against the dangers that would confront us in war.

In conclusion, there is one other land product—timber—which required an immense amount of tonnage during the war, but of which we are only just beginning to develop our capacities for production. It is mentioned here so that it may be borne in mind as an important ingredient in the programme of development that will be proposed. There are millions of acres of land well suited for timber production on commercial lines that are at present entirely waste.

PART III

SECTION II

Chapter XVI

Capacities and Employment

Productive Capacities of Arable and Grass Lands—Present Production
and Possible Increases—The Example of Denmark—
Present Supplies and Home Production—
1. Increase of Arable Land-Cultivation
2. Grass Land Improvement Programme—Their possible results
3. Increased Fruit and Vegetable Production—
Possible Forestry Extensions—Increases of Employment Through the
First Three Sections.

THE SPLENDID PRODUCTIVE capacity of our land
is an established fact. The question at the heart of the
agricultural problem is why it has been so neglected. The
answers to that question which I have endeavoured to provide have determined the form of the ways and means that
have been suggested for securing its proper utilisation.

We should now bring together in a concrete form an
estimate of the *capacity* of the land for useful production
and formulate, upon that basis, a plan of action designed
to secure its effective development. In doing so we need
not attempt to forecast the productive capacities that
science may make possible in the future, although we may
be quite sure on the evidence we now have that they will
far exceed anything that is realised at present.

One of the most remarkable and encouraging features
of the present situation is that, notwithstanding the
decline in cultivation and the proved neglect of millions
of acres, there was an increase, between 1931 and 1936,
of no less than 24 per cent in the output of human food per
100 acres, according to a research conducted by the
Agricultural Economics Institute at Oxford, although
there was a diminution in the output of animal feeding-
stuffs which called for additional importation.

The most important contributions to this result were the increased yield of milk per cow and other results that have followed improvements in the feeding of animals. Unfortunately it relates only to a small section of agriculture, but it does furnish some guide as to what could be done if we set about the business in earnest.

In his recent book on the "Hill-lands of Today", Professor Stapledon, when urging that increased rural population can only be obtained if measures are taken to increase soil fertility, says that "the creation of soil fertility has never been so easy or so cheap as today in this mechanical and technical age".[1] Sir Daniel Hall confirms this statement although in less emphatic terms, when he tells us that the land is still "a comparatively undeveloped national asset".[2]

The statements I am now going to make as to the productivity of arable and grassland represent the results that are common to the findings of many investigations, but I will be careful to understate rather than to overstate the case. In particular, use will be made of the definite conclusions of Sir Daniel Hall and Professor Stapledon.

In the old days 100 acres of arable land normally gave employment to six or seven men, and although instances can be given where, for certain purposes, that number, or even more, may be profitably employed, we must allow for the increased use of machinery. For present purposes, therefore, the number will be estimated as an average of four men per 100 acres of arable land.

It is not commonly realised that more animal food, as well as human food, is produced from land under arable cultivation, as compared with grass. Apart from what may be advantageously done for the best land suitable for remaining under grass, the fact is that, in the ordinary rotation of crops, as well as from the straw and other products, land under the plough yields a great deal more food per acre, both for man and beast, than when it is left down to grass.

[1] Page 27.
[2] *Agriculture after the War*, Sir A. D. Hall, K.C.B., F.R.S., John Murray, 1920, p. 17.

An acre of land under wheat will produce four quarters of grain and about $1\frac{1}{2}$ tons of straw, and Sir Daniel Hall says that if the whole of this material were fed to cattle it would produce the equivalent of 256 lbs. of meat or 360 gallons of milk.[1] The same acre of land under grass, even at a generous estimate, would produce only 120 lbs. of meat or 168 gallons of milk.

In this connection the allowance for the meat product made by Sir Daniel Hall on existing pastures substantially exceeds that of Professor Stapledon, who assesses the product of ordinary "fairly good pasture" at from 90 to 100 lbs. of meat.

If we extend this test to an acre of land under a six-year crop rotation (wheat (twice), barley, oats, roots and clover) the land will produce a *yearly* average of 660 lbs. of wheat and 330 lbs. of barley in addition to an increase of cattle weight of 155 lbs. derived from the consumption of the oats, roots and clover. These results are confirmed by those obtained by Mr. Middleton of the Ministry of Agriculture in 1915.

Put briefly, as a statement of the results which can be obtained by *present methods*, before any possible improvements have been adopted, the arable land of this country produces from $2\frac{1}{2}$ to 3 times as much cattle food per acre as permanent grass or, in terms of human and animal food together, will produce as much meat per acre as good grass, in addition to the corn and other foods provided for human consumption.

It is impossible to imagine a more desolating comment upon the existing state of affairs than that made by Sir Daniel Hall, who was, for many years, the chief scientific adviser to our Government on Agricultural questions, when, in concluding his review of this subject, he said:

"The bulk of the grassland of this country could, at best, only be described as useful, and with skilled management and a due expenditure upon Labour, would pay the farmers just as well under the plough,

[1] Loq. cit., pp. 31–2.

while it would yield for the nation more than twice as much food in the shape of meat or milk, or ten times as much in the form of grain."[1]

All land, in fact, is more productive if it is periodically ploughed, even the best fattening pastures, because when land has been left down for grass for many years the texture of the soil suffers, the aeration of the land becomes deficient and the herbage deteriorates in quality.

In the case of the best pastures, by careful management and generous manuring, a good volume of produce is obtained without ploughing, but a large proportion of the existing grassland would undoubtedly benefit by being ploughed on some such procedure as the following: The land would first be ploughed and then sown down with a good grass mixture; livestock would be kept on it for a term of years; it would then be ploughed up again and its fertility reaped in a good arable crop. The rotation then being repeated.

Before we come to a programme based on these findings, let us remind ourselves of what has already happened.

ACREAGE OF ARABLE LAND IN GREAT BRITAIN

				Acres
1891	.	.	.	16,484,664
1921	.	.	.	14,967,303
1931	.	.	.	12,634,358
1936	.	.	.	12,095,469

A diminution in the area of land under the plough of 4,389,195 acres.

There were no records of the extent of what are described as "rough grazings" before 1911, but since that time the acreage so described has increased by 2,968,517 acres, whilst the extent of grassland that is included in the "cultivated" area has increased by 925,880 acres. The balance has been absorbed by road widening and urban extensions, although

[1] Loq. cit., pp. 86–7.

the more precise returns of rough grazings that have been obtained since 1911 have probably led to the inclusion of some hill-lands that were previously not taken account of.

Bad as it is, the foregoing table does not reveal the full extent of the decline. Between 1872 and 1888 there were 18,600,000 acres under the plough in Great Britain and we are down now, as the table shows, to little over 12,000,000. There is no reason to doubt but that it would be profitable again to cultivate this eighteen million acres if there were behind it the cultural and marketing plans we ought to have. It should be emphasised also that, apart from the 17,359,730 acres of Permanent grass, there are nearly $5\frac{1}{2}$ million acres in England and Wales alone which are classified as "rough grazings" and their extent has been increasing yearly for some time past notwithstanding the diminution of the total area of land under cultivation and apart from land taken up by new roads, buildings and other urban enterprises.[1]

Let me now try to summarise for our guidance the reasons for this widespread and disastrous change.

The National policy during the past century was to encourage our development as a trading and industrial community, and let the land more or less take care of itself. The recurring depressions in agriculture, due to instability of prices, left the farming community as a whole, even when times were better, with little confidence of permanent improvement. Most farmers came to accept, with a sort of fatalistic acceptation, that slumps were inevitable, and, as a class, they were not disposed to respond to new opportunities or to be enterprising. They preferred to do things as far as possible "on the cheap". It is true that at all times there have been signal and encouraging exceptions, and if these exceptions had been the rule, there would have been no case for this book. In the main, however, farmers took the line of least risk when they found they could "get a living" by putting the land down to grass. It does not require so much capital, it takes less labour, and is attended with less risk. As Sir Daniel Hall puts it:—

[1] See Appendix II.

"His (the farmer's) personal profit does not coincide with the national interest either in the direction of the production of food or in the maintenance of men upon the land."[1]

At the back of this, all the time, has been the desolating influence of the *uncertainty* of price. Its effect has been manifest in depressing the standard both of farming and of the farmer and in intensifying his indisposition to make the best use of advancing knowledge or to apply new methods. In this way it has had a wholesale and continuously depressing effect upon the standard of enterprise. Keen young men have sought other openings and a large proportion of those that remained have preferred to take the least risk, so that "ranching" methods have been increasingly applied to vast extents of fertile land.

A dreadful case may be quoted from Sir Daniel Hall of a man who acquired by hiring or by purchase the control of 8,608 acres. The portion purchased was all laid down to grass. One section, which formerly consisted of five farms, totalling 1,360 acres, now employs only two men! Three of the farm-houses have been let as private residences and two are empty. On another section of 1,500 acres, four men only are employed where previously seventy found work, and on the remainder of the area, which was rented, the number employed has been reduced from 160 to 70.[2]

This is an extreme case, no doubt, but it should not be allowed to occur at all, and the folly of the system that permits of it is exposed every day by those cases in which the application of capital, brains and good organisation has been attended with precisely the opposite results.

Even if we were to bring again under the plough the full 18,000,000 acres that was formerly cultivated in that way, we should still have a percentage under cultivation less than neighbouring European countries.

Earlier on I referred to Denmark in connection with bacon production, but we ought not to lose sight of what has otherwise been achieved in that country by organised

[1] Loc. cit., p. 34.   [2] Loq. cit., pp. 61–2.

and sustained direction. The proportion of land now under the plough, or under rotation grasses, in that country has risen to 89 per cent of the total cultivated area, and the results are no less striking in the increased number of people "living by agriculture" than they are in the production of crops or the maintenance of live-stock.

The outstanding facts are as follows:—[1]

1. In 1871 the total cultivated area was 6,412,000 acres. In 1912 it had been extended to 7,289,000 acres.
2. In 1871 the corn and other crops occupied 1,837,000 acres; in 1912, 4,522,000 acres.
3. In 1871 the total number of cattle in the country was 1,238,898. In 1914 it had risen to 2,462,862.
4. In the same period the number of pigs had increased from 442,421 to 2,496,686.

During this period of development the number of persons living by agriculture had increased from 788,735 to 969,227.

Whilst Denmark, therefore, added 180,000 to the persons employed in agriculture, the numbers in Great Britain diminished by more than 300,000. In the one case there has been sustained leadership; in the other case, drift.

It is not that we could not have done as well ourselves. It is that we have not bothered. We are now in what is called prosperous times, but there is still a hard core of more than 1,500,000 unemployed, and they exist side by side with a source of undeveloped wealth in the land that is difficult to estimate because it is so large.

If it were developed it would of course provide an immense volume of employment not only for those engaged in land work but for a great variety of others in village, country town and factory who would benefit by the increased demands of a prosperous agriculture.

The country also, as we have seen, is in real need of a more abundant supply of the very products that our land is particularly fitted to produce, and in the case of

[1] The figures of the Danish development are taken from *Agriculture after the War*, by Sir A. D. Hall, pp. 99–103.

some of them the disaster of war would find us in a very precarious position. In these circumstances who can quarrel with Stapledon when he suggests that we are "stark, staring mad" to neglect our land in this way and to permit fertile soil to be treated as a ranch.

Unfortunately we cannot believe that the establishment of a reliable price-system with good marketing as a basis for the industry would be enough by itself. During the years before the war when agriculture as a whole was doing well, land still continued to be laid down to grass because a living could be got that way in place of more active cultivation.

We must therefore have a system under which we can plan for, and obtain, good cultivation and under which we deliberately encourage ability as well as the application of the lessons of science to the cultivation of the land.

It can be done. But it never will be done unless sufficient authority is possessed by those in charge; and unless capital and direction are supplied under skilled leadership.

"The State must intervene to bring about progress and not decay. . . . We have trusted to individual enterprise and self-interest as the only principles of action. Let us at least acknowledge their failure and resolve to take thought for the future."[1]

A Programme of Increased Food[2] Production

In attempting to express the possibilities of the land in terms of a programme of increased Food production, regard should be had not only to the increased food needs of the people and to the amount of stocks of the principal foods that ought normally to be held in the country for safety's sake, but to what ought to be done, in any case, to increase our present food production by using the land properly.

We have proved that the increased Food requirements of the people (if produced at home) would call for an addition to the present output as follows:—

[1] Sir Daniel Hall. Loc. cit., pp. 116–17.
[2] Increased Timber Production and Forestry are dealt with in Chapter XIX.

Of *Milk* for (liquid consumption,) Butter and
    Cheese 100%
Of Eggs 60%
Of Fruit 73%
Of Vegetables 60%
Of Meat 25%

The average stocks of food held in the country apart
from our own wheat and sugar harvests are:—

Wheat and Flour . . . . 6 weeks
Butter . . . . . . 2 weeks
Lard, Margarine and other fats . . 1 week
Sugar . . . . . . 1 week
Imported Meat . . . . 2 weeks
Eggs . . . . . . A few days.

Taking the whole year round, the present total supplies
and the percentage of them produced at Home are as
follows, if we allow for farm-produced butter and exclude
eggs imported in liquid and dry form and such fruits as
this country does not produce.

Total Supplies 1935

	Quantities	Percentage Home Produced
Wheat and Flour .	143,952,000 cwts.	21·9
Barley . .	31,747,000 cwts.	46
Oats . . .	39,924,000 cwts.	91
Beef and Veal .	25,507,121 cwts.	50
Mutton and Lamb	11,351,780 cwts.	43·6
Pig Meat . .	16,948,163 cwts.	48·4
Potatoes . .	3,350,773 tons	90·7
Eggs in Shell .	6,000 millions	55·7
Poultry . .	1,911,117 cwts.	77
Milk (Liquid) .	773,400,000 gallons	100
Butter . .	2,653,800,000 milk galls.	9
Cheese . .	411,900,000 milk galls.	30·2
Fruit (1936) . .	19,507,843 cwts.	64

	Quantities	*Persentage Home Produced*
Sugar (refined) .	38,442,030 cwts.	28·7
Market-Garden Produce with Tomatoes and Onions .	£30,435,000 value	82

The chief considerations group themselves around these three:—

1. The small proportion of wheat produced at home;
2. The increased requirement of animal products—milk, butter, fat, eggs and meat—and the demand for the animal feeding-stuffs their production would create; and
3. The increased need of vegetables and fruit.

The first two overlap and must be treated together; the third will be taken afterwards.
Increase of Arable Land and Grassland Improvements.

1. Increase of Arable Land

In the case of arable land we may, for present purposes take wheat production as the test, although in the course of rotation many other crops are grown. The present home production, which supplies less than a quarter of our requirements, is obtained from about 1,800,000 acres of wheat.

Sir Daniel Hall worked out a detailed scheme for the production of more than half our wheat requirements on an arable area of 18,000,000 acres.[1] At the time to which he referred there were 14,000,000 acres under the plough and the cultivated area of the whole country was about 32,000,000 acres. Both figures have dwindled. The cultivated area has now shrunk to 29,500,000 acres, and the arable to 12,000,000 so that the task of raising half our wheat at home is greater than it was.

For present purposes let us take a plan under which an additional 5,000,000 acres would be brought under the plough thus raising the arable area to 17,000,000 acres.

[1] Loc. cit., pp. 90–9.

It is not necessary to give particulars of the plan of cropping that would be followed; the reader who is interested is advised to study the detailed scheme Sir Daniel Hall puts forward. The number of wheat or other cereal crops that are taken during a rotation varies in different parts of the country. In some districts three cereal crops are taken during a five-year rotation—in others as many as four out of six, and it has been proved that by adequate manuring a succession of wheat crops can be grown. We may, however, regard excessive wheat cropping as a possible war-time emergency. The average appears to be 10 crops of wheat, barley or oats out of 17—the rest consisting of, say, 1 peas or beans; 3, of roots or potatoes; and 3, of clover or rotation grasses.

On this basis, and allowing for the production of about the present quantity of barley and for an increase of a third in oats, we should have an annual wheat acreage of more than 4,000,000 out of the 17,000,000 acres. This would provide for 45 per cent of our present total requirements and the cultivation of this increased arable area, as already explained would be accompanied by a production of animal food greater than is now obtained on the same land.

2. *Grassland Improvements*

In a recent address[1] Professor Stapledon said there were 10,000,000 acres of grassland that would be greatly improved by rotation ploughing. In any case we should contemplate the application of this method to the land that is now described as "rough grazing" to the extent of 5,000,000 acres, at least, in the whole of Great Britain. With regard to other grassland it will be sufficient for our present purposes if we allow for the application of Stapledon's methods to a further $2\frac{1}{2}$ million acres of what are now described as "moderate pastures".

The increase of yield per acre in terms of meat according to Professor Stapledon would be 70 lbs. for each acre of the rough grazing and 150 lbs. per acre for the better pastures.

[1] Address at the Chartered Surveyors' Institution, January 11th, 1938

If the increased meat yield was alternatively expressed in terms of milk it would, according to Sir Daniel Hall's calculations, be equivalent to an increased milk production of 90 gallons per acre on the rough grazing, and about 190 gallons on the better land.

The following table represents the results:—

Increased Meat Yield		lbs.	cwts.
5,000,000 acres @ 70 lbs.	=	350,000,000 =	3,125,000
2,500,000 acres @ 150 lbs.	=	375,000,000 =	3,348,214
		725,000,000	6,473,214

Or Alternatively in Terms of Milk:

Increased milk yield		Gallons
5,000,000 @ 90 gallons	=	450,000,000
2,500,000 @ 190 gallons	=	475,000,000
		925,000,000

This means that by the improved treatment of these $7\frac{1}{2}$ million acres of grass alone, if they were so used, we could obtain (according to the calculations already made[1]) the full increase of milk supplies that the people need for liquid consumption and, beyond that, sufficient milk to provide for an increase of nearly 25 per cent in our present total supplies of butter thereby increasing by three times the amount of butter now made from home supplies of milk. It would, unfortunately, be some years at the best before such an increased consumption could become possible, but it would have the effect all the time of making us less dependent on outside supplies, and at the same time we should be putting the land to a better use.

In addition to this, if we take account of the increased meat-producing power that the extra 5,000,000 acres of arable land would provide us with, we should be able by these two enterprises alone to meet more than the extra demand that an adequate nutritional policy would require

[1] See Chapter XV pp. 198–200.

both in meat and milk products and at the same time secure the invaluable addition of more than twice our present output of wheat and all that it would carry with it of increased animal feeding-stuffs.

At the same time, of course, the national plan under which these improvements would be fostered would extend its encouragement of better methods to the land that is now under arable cultivation as well as to other grasslands. We may be sure that the increase in productive capacity that recent years have witnessed would, and certainly could, be greatly increased on these other lands.

Indeed, as I said before, the increased productive capacity of our land is difficult to estimate because it is so great.

3. *Vegetable and Fruit Production*

This, third section, of a development programme applies to products that we can grow easily in this country, and their cultivation provides for much employment.

The chief drawback is the dreadful state of the existing marketing arrangements and the absence of good storage facilities. These would have to be tackled as soon as possible, but, apart from them, increased cultivation could quickly be arranged for.

It will be necessary to consider details when we come to examine the possibilities of Smallholdings and other ways of promoting intensive cultivation. But a general programme is not difficult to forecast.

The present acreage devoted to the production of vegetables for the market is rather more than 250,000 acres, and the acreage devoted to orchards and to small fruit is about 300,000 acres.

We have found that, on nutritional grounds, the people require an increase of 73 per cent of home-grown fruit and 60 per cent of vegetables. It is evident, therefore, that from the beginning we should aim for an addition of 400,000 acres devoted to the production of fruit and vegetables, especially if it proves to be a fact, as stated, that the London market alone, for winter salads, could absorb the product of some 20,000 acres cultivated intensively under Dutch lights or in some such way.

One of the most remarkable facts in this connection, on the vegetable side, is our almost complete dependence for onions upon outside supplies. In 1936 the home production for the market was less than 120,000 cwts, whilst imported supplies amounted to 10,434,628 cwts. Good, long-keeping varieties of the onion grow very well indeed in some districts of this country, and, so far, I have not found a reliable and sufficient explanation of this trivial home production.

The amount of labour that vegetable and fruit cultivation require is much greater than that needed for arable cultivation in the ordinary rotation. When the cultivation is intense, as when glass is used, the numbers employed are very high, but in order to keep our estimates on the moderate side I have chosen a case in which vegetables are largely grown for the London and other markets and where mechanical aids are made the most use of. The Fordson Estates in Essex, to which reference will be made in a later chapter, are a good example of this kind of cultivation and warrant the estimate of an average of seven persons employed full time per 100 acres.

4. *Forestry*

A fourth section of the Development Programme for which we are already provided with reliable data, is that of Forestry. The extension of this work and the gradual concomitant increase of employment necessarily occupies a period of time much longer than that required for the first three sections that we have been examining in this chapter, and it will be better to treat it separately.

I may say, however, that the ultimate afforestation of the land, not usable for any other purpose so far as can be seen at present, will be estimated on a conservative basis to provide constant employment for not less than 85,000 additional men at the expiration of the full eighty-year period of forestry development.[1]

[1] Details of this estimate will be found in Chap: XIX pp. 270–273.

Labour Requirements—First three sections of the Programme

The estimate of the Labour requirements of fruit and vegetable culture enables me to bring together in terms of additional labour what would be required for the first three main parts of the plan of development we have been considering. In each case the figures are given at a low estimate and it ought to be emphasised that each of the undertakings is undeniably one that present practice and experience show to be justified, and well in accord with the proved facts of our productive capacities.

The following table shows the results:—

	Increased number of wholetime workers
1. 5,000,000 acres of arable land; 4 men per 100 acres in place of 1 at present.	150,000
2. Rotation grass ploughing of 7,500,000 acres: 1 man per 100 acres instead of 1 man per 200 acres at present	37,000
3. 400,000 acres additional vegetable and fruit acreage: 7 men per 100 acres instead of 3 at present	16,000
Total	203,000

It is obvious that these figures take account only of those for whom full-time employment would be provided and are far from expressing the additional employment that would be created. There would be an enormous volume of additional seasonal labour on the land itself and all the extra work that would be provided in transport and in a great variety of manufactures, such as in the making of packing materials, agricultural implements, canning and in other ways, apart entirely from the labour employed on capital improvements such as new cottages, improved farm buildings, drainage, water supplies and the rest.

Let us now examine the ways and means that should be adopted to give effect to these plans.

PART III

SECTION III

Chapter XVII

The Extension of Arable Farming and Grassland Improvement

Preliminary Considerations—*Cereal Price Policy*—
1. *Tenant Farming :* The Farmers and the Programme—The Assistance that would be rendered.
2. *Large-Scale Farming :* The Method Proposed—Examples—More Production—More Employment—Better Wages.
3. *Demonstration Farms.*

ANY PLAN THAT aims at securing that the land should be used for what it will best yield by good cultivation rather than for obtaining some sort of a profit with the minimum of labour, can only be carried out if we have a suitable Central Authority with continuing powers.

This will apply to the proposals outlined in the previous chapter or to any others that might be substituted for them.

Up to the present we have spoken of the Central Authority as the National Agricultural Commission and visualised it as having general charge, through appropriate organisations, of the operations concerned, including land development and equipment, marketing, storage policy and the rest.

I will postpone a forecast of the Departmental arrangements that might be called for, but it is evident that, both in the persecution of the plan for extended cultivation and in securing better equipment, the Central Authority would have to be served by a very competent staff. It must be able to command the services of experts in different branches of agriculture, of scientists, of experienced surveyors and land agents, engineers, foresters and others. The preparation of such a plan would also call for much work on the spot in the different Counties, in co-operation with the County Committees, particularly with regard to the allocation of increased areas to arable farming, the planning of the grassland improvement, and so forth. Much of the work would probably have to be done on a regional rather than a county basis.

The preparation of such a plan would be a great task, especially in view of the deplorable condition of much of the land and of the large expenditure that would be required in some districts in improvement in buildings and in other forms of equipment. It would be a many-sided task and would call for progressive enquiries and research, as well as for the advice and assistance of experts in different branches of cultivation.

It is necessary also that the scheme should be one which will encourage enterprise and keenness throughout the industry.

There is no doubt that one of the biggest drawbacks in farming today has been the hopelessness of the outlook that is presented to young men who may have good ability but no capital. We ought to be able to develop a plan of operations that will attract such men and give them an opportunity. At the present time the prospect for those who pass through the Agricultural Colleges or Institutes, as well as for many other competent young men, is very poor indeed. Except for appointments under County Councils, a few teaching posts, or work abroad, there are practically no openings for them. This is a terrible defect in agriculture. The leaders in every other big industry are always on the look out for well-trained young men with the right kind of ability, and we must devise a system in agriculture that will attract brains to the service of its re-generation. There are plenty of brains to be attracted. They must be given a chance.

The following appear to be the directions in which the Central Authority would work:—

1. The encouragement and assistance of tenant farmers.
2. A sufficient development of Large-scale farming.
3. The establishment of suitable Demonstration farms.
4. The encouragement of Small-scale farming or intensive cultivation in different ways.
5. Adding to the area of cultivatable land by Reclamation when practicable.

6. Increased Forestry work with which I will associate the preservation of country-side beauty and the extension of amenities.

I propose to devote this Chapter to a consideration of the first three named after a preliminary reference to Cereal Price Policy.

Cereal Price Policy

It is impossible to expect sustained development if the chief cereal crop—wheat—is sold as low as 20s. a quarter at one time, or as high as 60s. at another with all sorts of variations in between.

This is what has happened in the past.

The nominal price at which wheat is now stabilised, 45s. per quarter, is higher than it need be. It was found conclusively in the enquiries that were made during 1930 and 1931 that some efficient producers, who kept proper accounts, were producing wheat profitably at round about 37s. a quarter, and no stabilised price system would be tolerated for long that did not require efficiency. Nevertheless it is certain that stabilisation of the price of wheat is absolutely essential as an ingredient in a plan of increased arable cultivation.

The precise level must be one that is the result of competent and impartial enquiry, but, judging from the evidence available in 1931, it is probable that with the other measures of assistance to improve cultivation that would be associated with the whole scheme, a price of about 37s. 6d. per quarter would be sufficient. In any case, as already explained, the price control must be associated with efficient machinery for securing economies in distribution and for safeguarding the consumer in regard to bread prices.

The proposal made in the previous chapter was to raise the wheat acreage to four million out of seventeen million acres to be devoted to arable cultivation. This represents a twenty-three percentage of arable land devoted to wheat, against the fifteen per cent cultivated in that way at present. In former times the proportion of wheat to the rest of arable was 24 per cent so that the figure proposed is not excessive in view of the help that would be provided in other directions.

The other two chief cereal crops are Barley and Oats. The lower grade barleys are mostly used for animal feeding and the higher grade, or malting qualities, for brewing. I have in my possession the preliminary details of a scheme for securing a stable price for good quality barley through the co-operation of the Customs and Excise in a scheme operating through the brewing trade. There is undoubtedly room in the price of beer to pay a fair and stable price for malting barley and it would not be difficult to establish a workable scheme. Lower-grade barleys would have to be sold at competitive world prices, subject in any case to well-arranged marketing operations that would safe-guard the producer from speculative price interference. We may anticipate that there would be a substantial increase in the acreage devoted to oats, particularly perhaps in Scotland, but it does not appear that any artificial aid, apart from well-organised marketing operations, would be called for. Our pre-eminence in oat production during recent years does not seem to have been much affected. We still produce 91 per cent of our total requirements.

It would not be difficult, by arrangements with existing trade channels, to establish good marketing arrangements, so far as the primary sales are concerned, for the other seed products of arable cultivation such as beans and peas.

There is complete unanimity amongst those who have investigated these problems, that the key to increased arable cultivation, so far as prices are concerned, is to be found in wheat, and it is the crop with which the consuming public is mainly concerned. We may therefore take it that, if the problem of wheat prices is satisfactorily dealt with, we can plan a large extension of arable acreage.

1. The Tenant Farmer

Although there ought to be, and doubtless will be, a great extension of large-scale farming operations, the bulk of the cultivation, so far as any present plan can estimate, will be through the farmer, who, under the scheme we are proposing, would be the tenant of State-owned land.

Some writers are inclined to put the blame for a large proportion of the present decline upon the quality of the individual farmer. Often enough, no doubt, this charge is well founded. They have been slow to make use of increased knowledge, to study or adopt new methods, and far too apt, through their representatives, to hold out their hand to the Government and to put the blame on the State without examining the extent to which they themselves, as a class, have incurred a share of the responsibility. For all that, speaking generally, I think they have been more sinned against than sinning. They have been subject to periodic slumps, together with the lack of any considered policy for their industry, whilst the best thought and purpose of the country has been devoted to the extension of industrial enterprise and to the encouragement of the export trade.

I believe, therefore, that the system here being advocated, under competent leadership, would evoke a widespread response from tenant farmers.

At the same time the State cannot acquiesce in bad farming, and the sort of cases to which reference has already been made, where neglect is a standing scandal and may have been so for years, would be those in which the National Authority would step in at once and make its own arrangements for cultivation. Judging from what happened in the war-time we may be sure that the County Committees, as a result of the surveys that would be made, would be able to furnish the Commission with several cases.

The proposals for the increase of arable acreage would be worked out by the experts employed, in association with the County Committees, so as to assess the proportion that might be contributed by the different counties or regions. Much relevant information is already available and a provisional plan of development would be worked out and allotted for the different areas.

So far as the ploughing of grassland is concerned, the amount of land which has reverted to rough grazings during recent years is readily ascertainable. In some districts, particularly in the hill districts Professor Stapledon specially writes about, the case would require to be dealt with on a Regional, rather than on a County, basis. Professor Stapledon tells us that in some districts "the farmlands could be doubled, and often comparatively easily".[1]

The whole scheme of increased cultivation would be a work of such magnitude, that the physical difficulties, in terms of men and machinery, for getting the work done would be the limiting factors for some years to come. Machinery would be used extensively and to a large extent it would have to be provided by the Central Authority, but when the fullest allowance has been made for this, we should find that the shortage most difficult to make up for would be that which has arisen out of our past neglect, namely that of skilled workmen with decent houses for them to live in. In any case the improvement of grasslands must be on a long-term programme and could only be undertaken and carried through by special assistance for the cultural operations being made available to existing tenants, or by considerable areas being undertaken by the National Commission itself under the operations that will be discussed in the next section of this chapter.

Many other forms of assistance to tenants would be provided through the agencies of the Central Authority apart from the capital provided to finance estate improvements, buildings, drainage, roads, water supplies, fencing, and the rest. One of the most valuable would be the provision of Short-term credit to enable occupiers to obtain good breeding stocks for their increased live-stock requirements, assistance in the purchase of fertilisers, and in other ways. This, in the main, would be arranged for through applications made by tenants and upon reports made by the appropriate staff, as has been the case in well-managed estates in times past in dealing with applications for capital improvements.

For some years to come the provision of better farm equipment will be one of the most urgent as well as one

[1] Loc. cit., p. 76.

of the most necessary tasks of our National Commission. In order to have the work well managed, appropriately sized estate units would have to be arranged for. It is commonly said that a unit of 30,000 acres is about the size that an efficient staff can deal with. The size of the unit, however, would necessarily vary with the character of the district and with the standard of present farming efficiency. In any case it would be through the Estates Department that the requirements of cultivators for capital improvements would be dealt with after the plan of local development had been considered by the County Committee.

To come back to the general theme of this section, my conclusion is that it would be possible, through a sensibly formulated plan, to secure its execution with the goodwill and the co-operation of a large proportion of existing farmers. Everywhere one goes, despite fashionable grumbles, you can find able and intelligent farmers who would be keen to co-operate, and the work of the County Committees and the propaganda on behalf of the Plan that would necessarily be instituted would enable the leaven of their influence to spread.

In any case we cannot produce capable cultivators, either farmers or labourers, quickly; as many a man has found to his cost who had the notion that he could soon pick up farming. It would therefore be to ask for failure if the Commission and the County Committees did not do their utmost to secure the hearty co-operation of capable cultivators.

2. *Large-Scale Farming*

A proposal for the establishment of a Large-Scale Farming Corporation with a million pounds capital was embodied in the Land Utilisation Bill as introduced by me into Parliament in November 1930, but it had, unfortunately, to be dropped in the House of Lords as the price of saving the Bill.

So far as the Debates in either Houses were concerned there was no substantial case made against the proposal. The Opposition entirely rested upon objection to its "Socialistic" character. There was nothing new about the suggestion at all. It has been a method strongly recommended for a long time past by men of all kinds of political attachments purely on the merits of the case. There are many illustrations of the success of this method of farming under experienced management, and it certainly ought to be widely extended.

It is not denied that the present occupiers are very often deficient in working capital and unable on that account either to maintain land fertility or to stock and farm the land as it should be farmed, so that we are presented with cheap farming and scanty production over large areas of land alongside a standard of management that is often low. There is no organisation in agriculture comparable with that which any other industry of the same magnitude possesses, and there is an urgent need for the introduction into it of a type of organisation which is big enough to make use of the best ability available, to employ proper accounting and make use of the expert knowledge that is at our disposal. Certain obvious advantages attach to a well-managed, large-scale organisation equipped with sufficient capital, and they are just as applicable to agriculture as to anything else.

There are hundreds of farms which are not big enough to employ machinery to its proper capacity, and for months on end we may see expensive implements idle, and often left rusting out-of-doors. Large organisations also can employ skilled assistance in buying and selling, and benefit by the advantages that necessarily arise therefrom. Similarly they are able to secure economical and skilled assembly of produce together with good grading, packing and transport. At the same time in many cases there is a great waste on the land by a multiplicity of fences and smallness of the fields accompanied by defective farm communications, with much loss of efficiency.

In agriculture, as in other industries, large-scale enterprises can afford efficient direction, scientific advice and the proper book-keeping and accounting which are so conspicuously absent today.

There is nothing new about any of this. How would

any other business expect to prosper unless it had the advantage of good accounting methods to reveal its waste, to suggest economies and to direct its efforts in the most profitable direction? The same principles of sound management apply, not with less, but with more force to a complicated industry like agriculture where all manner of different procedures are being undertaken and diverse crops being produced or arranged for at the same time.

The real reason why this kind of thing has not prevailed in agriculture is that we have sought to attract the brains and capital of the country to manufacturing and industrial enterprises. Our eyes have been upon the ends of the earth rather than upon our own fields.

Another advantage that would attach to this form of development would be that it would provide an opening and a training ground for large numbers of the capable young men I have already referred to who are shut out at present because they have no capital. It would enable us to create the "ladder" that is so urgently needed.

Moreover the circumstances that would arise as soon as the State became the owner of the land would almost compel the adoption of some such system as this because of the conditions with which the Central Organisation would find itself confronted. Nearly a million acres of what was once accounted good land have disappeared entirely from cultivation, apart from the inroads of towns, new roads, and development generally. Furthermore some five to eight per cent of agricultural tenancies fall in every year in addition to which the National Commission would be confronted up and down the country with an immense acreage of land that would require restoration. The cost of cleaning this land and putting it into good condition, restoring its drainage, and providing it with proper fences, farm roads and buildings would necessarily fall upon the Commission. It is a form of capital outlay that has got to be incurred on such land before it can be farmed properly.

Apart, therefore, from the fact that large-scale operations are justifiable in themselves and badly needed, it would, in many cases, present the easiest, if not the only way, of securing good cultivation on much vacant land.

As I have said before, we are already provided with a goodly number of instances of the success of this method. It may be interesting to mention a few.

Professor Orwin gives some striking instances in his book on "The Future of Farming". One of the most remarkable cases is that of the intensive arable cultivation of a large area of land by Mr. Baylis. It was started in a small way in 1851 and has steadily been increased by adding other farms as they became vacant. The result, as stated by Orwin, is that "Today there are no less than 22 farms in his occupation extending to more than 12,000 acres and of half this area he is owner as well as occupier. This vast enterprise, unique in England, which is still being carried on, has been built up entirely under a system of specialisation in arable crop production."[1] As an instance of the kind of thing that occurs as agricultural holdings become vacant, Professor Orwin reports that Mr. Baylis claims that he has never dispossessed another farmer who was both able and willing to carry on and that several of his farms were taken over from mortgagees in possession or even in a condition actually derelict.

Another interesting case quoted by Professor Orwin is that of the enterprise of Mr. F. P. Chamberlain on Crowmarsh Battle Farm in Wiltshire since 1894. This is an example of specialist arable farming successfully continued for a long period of years on the basis (to quote Mr. Chamberlain) that "a farmer should be as far as possible a chemist and a botanist, but above all he should be an accountant".[2] He has relied largely on artificial manures and on the turning-in of clover to maintain soil fertility and humus, with reliance upon mechanical power for tillage operations; the whole process being based upon a scientific examination of possibilities, and, above all, on accurate cost accounting.

Amongst the other cases quoted by Professor Orwin, one of the most interesting is that of the grassland experiments

[1] Loc. cit., p. 65.   [2] Loc. cit., p. 73.

of Mr. Stanley Bligh in increasing the stock-carrying capacity of what was previously poor land.

These cases, however, are instances of successful specialised farming. They may be supplemented by three instances of mixed farming quoted by Sir Daniel Hall, with fuller details of one that was thoroughly investigated when we were examining this method previous to the introduction of the Land Utilisation Act.

The three cases that I will quote from Sir Daniel Hall[1] are taken because they each make a separate allowance for management expenses. The first case was that of a farm of 4,000 acres, two-thirds arable. The capital per acre was about £10; the number of men employed, 5 per 100 acres; an allowance of 10s. per acre, or £2,000 a year, was made for management; 5 per cent was paid on capital, and the profits for some years prior to the outbreak of war, in addition, were 10·5 per cent. In the second case the farm was of 5,000 acres, three-fourths arable; the capital per acre was about £8; the number of men employed was 4 per 100 acres; the management allowance was 5s. per acre, or £1,250 a year, with an average profit, after paying 5 per cent on capital, of 12½ per cent. The third case was that of a smaller farm of 1,500 acres in which the capital was estimated at £12 per acre; the number of men employed was 7 per 100 acres; the management allowance was 5s. per acre, or £375 per annum, and the profit, after paying 5 per cent on capital, was 10 per cent.

In respect of these three cases it should be mentioned that the wages were low during those years, the average earnings per man being only from 21s. 6d. to 23s. a week, and we cannot contemplate as satisfactory a standard of wages of that kind. Nevertheless with prices as they were during some of those years, and with profits earned over and above the allowances for management and after 5 per cent had been paid on capital, it is evident that there was a considerable margin for payment of better wages.

[1] *Agriculture After the War*, p. 43 *et seq.*

The case which I will now quote, however, covers a series of post-war years up to 1930 and provides an example of mixed, large-scale, farming under first-rate management which paid average wages of 42s. 3d. per week and still left a good profit in every year except one—and even in that year 5 per cent was paid on capital, beside a salary of £1,000 a year to the manager.

It provides a good illustration of what brains and capital can do together on land which, before the enterprise was embarked on, was mostly indifferently farmed by struggling occupiers.

The records were investigated at the time I was preparing the Utilisation of Land Act of 1931.

There were originally twenty-five separate farms. After purchase they were amalgamated and came to form a more or less rectangular block of land about six miles long and nearly two miles wide, comprising, in all, 6,366 acres. One block of it, comprising 3,564 acres, is completely arable in blocks of about 25 acres. Another part, comprising 1,119 acres, is kept under well-cultivated grass except for 109 acres of arable; the remainder is arable and is divided into fields of about 40 acres each. A light railway was laid the whole length of the estate by their own workmen at a cost of £24,000. Central buildings were created with a large mill containing provision for the storage of about 8,000 quarters of wheat, with grain conditioning apparatus, dressing machines, dust extractors, grinding mill, etc. The necessary machinery and electric light plants were provided, with a manager's office and other buildings, at a cost in all of a further £24,000. In addition to this, various shops for blacksmiths, fitters, motor repair and carpentry work were provided, with stores for dead stock, at a cost of £8,000.

The greater part of the arable land is farmed on a four-course rotation with

(1) A leguminous crop or clover
(2) Potatoes, or beet or mangels
(3) Wheat
(4) Oats or barley.

Most of the remainder of the arable land is worked on a longer rotation of

(1) Beet, potatoes or roots
(2) Wheat, barley or oats
(3) Clover, with two years grass or sanfoin, two years mown
(4) Peas for packeting
(5) Barley or wheat.

Intenser cultivation has meant a large increase in the number of livestock and, at the time at which the record was taken, there were 254 horses, 412 cattle, 1,664 sheep, and 1,978 pigs with 1,257 poultry.

Machinery of various kinds is extensively used; but, notwithstanding this, the results in terms of labour are as follows:—

There are 34 per cent more men employed full-time on the land than there were in the previous twenty-five farms, and 80 per cent more casual labour employed in connection with pea-sticking, potato crops, beet, etc. Not only is more labour employed, but the average wages came out at 42s. 3d. per week, whilst the average County rate at that time was 32s. per week. In this connection it is interesting to notice that all the mechanical work, running the railway, attending to the motors, machinery and the rest is performed by the farm employees. There is one expert foreman for the machine shops, another foreman for estate work and seven for different branches of the farm work.

The Manager, who is a well-educated man with excellent experience of practical farming and, happily, combines with these advantage the possession of first-rate organising and administrative ability, is paid £1,000 a year with a share of profit after 5 per cent has been paid on the full capitalised value of the whole undertaking.

The valuation of the whole undertaking, including all the capital works already mentioned, tenant-right, live and dead stock of all kinds, was somewhat under £130,000.

The whole concern has been running for several years and has never failed to pay the full 5 per cent, and for most years the Manager has had a substantial bonus as his share of the extra profits.

The success of this case depends from first to last upon highly skilled and capable management supported by an owner who is fortunately able to supply capital and foresight in abundance.

Another exceedingly interesting and encouraging fact emerged from an examination of this case where the utmost possible use is made of the land for crops and live-stock production as well as in the utilisation of the animal foods that are produced. It is that, notwithstanding the full utilisation of produce for feeding stock, the cash receipts for sales in the year ending May 31st, 1930, exceeded £100,000 and the returns per acre amounted to the satisfactory figure of £16 14s. 3d. on the whole estate.

This is a remarkable return when one compares it with the records, obtained by the investigations of the Cambridge University Agriculture Department, of the results on twenty-four separate farms in East Anglia for the years 1923 to 1927. The gross output per acre on these farms averaged £10 7s. per annum. On the basis of output per whole-time worker the East Anglican farms showed a product of £258, whilst on the large-scale farm, of which I have given particulars, the output was £464 per whole-time worker per annum.

It may be mentioned, parenthetically, that the average size of the farms investigated by the Cambridge University Enquiry was 230 acres.

Sir Daniel Hall makes a critical examination of the possibilities of this type of farming[1] and comes to the conclusion that a farming unit of about 5,000 acres should be the one to be aimed at, with variations up to 8,000 acres in some districts, or down to 3,000 in others.

He makes a generous allowance for the costs of management and expert assistance, including in that term technical and machinery management as well as accounting, and puts aside 10s. an acre for these purposes.

[1] Loc. cit., pp. 43-52.

In the case I have quoted, the management costs were substantially less than the allowance made by Sir Daniel Hall, but, whatever the amount may be, the important thing is that the concern should be big enough to allow for the employment on good terms of highly qualified management.

The scheme contemplated in the 1931 Act was the formation of a Farming Corporation with capital provided by the State in the form of a Public Utility Corporation. I think that organisations on these lines will be found to be the most useful mode of operation. It would probably be best for the National Commission to establish a number of separate Corporations, each in charge of their own large-scale farms, rather than to concentrate the work in the hands of a single great Corporation which might be too far removed from the realities on the spot and become too bureaucratic.

The limiting factor for some time to come may be the difficulty of obtaining competent management—which is a *sine qua non*. Opportunity, as we know, often calls out the best, and it might be so in this case. Let us hope it would; but I cannot help thinking that, owing to our past neglect of training men and giving them an opportunity, the difficulty of obtaining suitable personnel would be an obstacle for some time.

There is no necessity to forecast the area of land which would be farmed on these lines. We may be sure that it would rapidly increase. There would be more land calling for it in the early years than the National Commission would be able to undertake, although a large amount of the rotation grass-ploughing, as well as the increase of arable acreage, would be dealt with by tenant farmers.

3. *Demonstration Farms*

A good many people have forgotten, and no wonder, that under the present law the Minister of Agriculture has power to establish Demonstration farms. It was one of the clauses that I managed to get through Parliament in the Land Utilisation Act of 1931, and it may be worth while quoting Section I of Clause I that deals with it.

"1. (1) The Minister shall have power to purchase land or to take land on lease by agreement and to equip and hold land for the purpose of utilising the land as demonstration farms conducted on an economic basis under the management and control, as agents for the Minister, of local authorities, universities, agricultural colleges, or other bodies, or of any persons who, in the opinion of the Minister, are qualified to manage and control such farms and to give instruction in agricultural subjects."

This is the Law now. But it has not been applied. It was admitted on all hands at the time the subject was under discussion that farms of this character should be provided, and I find it difficult to describe in civil terms the neglect that has been displayed.

It was further provided that the Demonstration farms should not exceed 250 acres in extent and farms of that size would be sufficient for the purpose. We ought to have a number of such farms up and down the country devoted to appropriate branches of agriculture, to which farmers, and especially young farmers, smallholders and farm labourers, as well as students, would have free access. Nobody disputes that they are very much needed and that, if properly directed, they would be widely appreciated and used. They could, as the Act provides, be associated either with existing Colleges or Institutes, or separately established. The County Committees would soon see that the facilities for the use of them were made easy, and there is no doubt that they would be immensely serviceable to thousands of farmers in enabling them to see at first-hand what could be done and how it was done.

The establishment of a number of them would be an early undertaking of the National Commission so as to provide training grounds for the kind of men the industry must have if Agriculture is to be the field of activity and enterprise it ought to be.

PART III

SECTION IV

Chapter XVIII

The Extension of Cultivation for Market Garden and Fruit Production

Land Settlement Projects and Small-holdings—*Family Farms and Small-holdings*—The Conditions of Life—Mr. Lloyd George's Proposals in 1930—Experiences of the Land Settlement Association—*Grouped Small-holdings*—Advantage of that System—*Large-scale Enterprises*—The Fordson Estates—Concluding Recommendations.

Increased Production of Fruit and Vegetables

THE NEXT PART of our programme of increased production is designed to meet the needs of the people for fruit and vegetables. The 400,000 acres proposed represent a somewhat larger area than the actual increased needs of the people would demand if imports are to remain as at present, but our apples and other fruit are second to none and there is no reason at all why we should not produce a large proportion of the seven million cwts. we now import. An extra acreage is allowed for on that account.

During recent years an increased proportion of the supplies of home-grown fruit and vegetables has come from large farms. During the ten years previous to 1933 the acreage devoted to the production of Brussels Sprouts increased from about 17,000 to nearly 36,000 acres, and almost the whole of it was provided by large farms. Similar developments apply to other vegetables and to fruit. It is also the case that only about 17 per cent of existing Small-holdings are devoted to Market-Garden produce, so that, in considering the ways and means of increasing this type of production, we must look beyond Small-holdings. As, however, we are to consider intensive forms of production generally it will be convenient before going further to consider

QA

Small-holding and kindred schemes of "land settlement" in some detail.

Small-holdings

Most of the discussions in Parliament in recent years on "back to the land" questions, have dealt with the possibilities of increasing the number of land workers by Small-holdings.

They have manifested a strange disregard of the more immediate and bigger possibilities that would arise out of improved cultivation generally on planned and well-directed lines such as I have purposely put in the forefront. (Chapter XVII).

The limiting factor in this case, even more than that dealt with in the previous chapter, will be the shortage of efficient agricultural labourers and of decent houses for them to live in. I shall return to this question later on, but it must be borne in mind all the time that the replacement of efficient workers will call for special, almost for heroic, measures in regard to housing.

Small-holdings and Land Settlement

In 1930 Mr. Lloyd George submitted to the Government a number of detailed proposals for dealing with Unemployment, one of the most important of which was a proposal to settle 100,000 families in from three to five years, as small-holders or family farmers, on three million acres of land. It was a bold proposal, which, in many respects, failed to take account of limiting realities, but it was a significant illustration of the importance that has been attached to this method of increasing employment on the land.

Let us remind ourselves of the facts of the case as they are at present.

A Small-holding is one that is from one to fifty acres in extent, and there are, at present, some 280,000 of them in Great Britain. They comprise about 17 per cent of the area of the cultivated land in England and Wales and about 19 per cent in Scotland.

During recent years the numbers of Small-holdings below twenty acres has decreased and those between twenty and fifty acres have increased, mainly by the absorption of smaller holdings. The decline in the smaller holdings has been chiefly in those devoted to poultry or to fruit and vegetables.

Dairy-farming occupies the chief place in small-holdings. About 28 per cent of our dairy herds are on small-holdings, and the proportions of holdings of fifty acres or less devoted to dairying is 48 per cent of the total. Dairying, with mixed corn, pig and poultry production, as well as stock-raising, account for another 35 per cent.

The majority consist of what are known as "Family Farms", that is, of holdings worked by the occupier alone or by the aid of members of his family. In some parts of Wales the proportion of holdings worked by relatives is 44 per cent of the holdings. In Somerset, Devon and Cornwall it varies from 16 per cent to 24 per cent, whilst in the Eastern counties, where larger farms predominate, the propostion of holdings carried on in this way is about 6 per cent.

Of the total number of 280,000 Small-holdings or Family Farms only about 30,000 have been provided under the various Small-holdings Acts by County Councils since 1908. The number provided in 1936 was 1,235, although not all of them were new holdings, whilst the number of unsatisfied applicants was 7,481.

The amount of employment that Small-holdings provide appears to be about 2½ times as much on the average as that which was previously provided on the same land. These figures were carefully examined in a large number of cases for me in 1930 and 1931 and records were obtained of thirty-five different County Council estates comprising nearly 17,000 acres. They showed that the resident popula-iton on these Council lands had increased from 1,048 to 2,298 and on the Ministry's own estates from 490 to 1,227.

Reports also show that Small-holders have stood up to adversity very well. There were few cases of failures amongst the 14,000 small-holders established by Councils before the war, and even amongst those that were established in the rush after the war, when a great many men took up the work without adequate training or experience, we could not find that there had been more than 15 per cent who had failed to make good. The biggest proportion of failures was on poultry holdings.

One of the chief facts about this type of cultivation, and upon which the advocates of small-holdings rely, is the extraordinarily small proportion of our land that is devoted to this type of cultivation. In Germany nearly half the cultivated land is so used, and in France nearly 30 per cent, and this accounts for the much greater proportion of the employed population of those countries that is engaged in agriculture. It is highest in France where it is 41·9 per cent; in Germany it is 30·5 per cent,[1] whilst in Great Britain it is only 7·2 per cent.

The explanation of the small numbers in Great Britain lies in the history and policy of this country to which reference has so often been made, as well as to our system of land owning. Notwithstanding this, the number of small-holders in this country would undoubtedly be many more than they are if all the County Councils had been as active as Norfolk, the Isle of Ely, Bedford and Cambridge.

Some districts are unsuited for Small-holdings; but when this has been said and fully allowed for, the fact is that for years past there has been a waiting list of those who are regarded as "approved" applicants of 5,000 or more, and many men who want holdings have not troubled to apply because of the uselessness of doing so.

In the Land Utilisation Act 1931 powers were conferred upon the Minister to provide Small-holdings where the County Councils were failing to exercise the powers that Parliament had conferred upon them, and if these powers had been exercised by the present Government we should certainly find by now that the number of small-holdings would be substantially greater than it is.

[1] This was the figure previous to the present régime in Germany. I have no reliable figures as to what it is at present.

In order to become "approved", applicants have to show that they have already had practical experience of cultivation work, so that it is not surprising that 62 per cent of the existing small-holders are sons of farmers, small-holders or agricultural labourers, and that a further 13 per cent have previously pursued some rural occupation. The small proportion of those (16 per cent) who previously had urban occupations only is mainly accounted for by the settlements which were made after the war. Unfortunately these men provided a great majority of those who failed to succeed after the war, although I recall that one of the most successful small-holders on the Ministry of Agriculture's Estate near Holbeach had been driving a four-wheel cab in the City before the war. But he seemed to me to be the sort of man who would be likely to succeed at nearly any job he took up.

There is no means of knowing what the number of suitable applicants would have been if all the County Councils had been equally keen on the work. All we know is that the waiting list seems to fluctuate around 5,000.

The solid fact, however, is that after nearly thirty years of effort, often admittedly very languid, we have only settled, through public effort, rather less than 30,000 families on a little over 460,000 acres of land. In more than half these cases, also, the expression "settled" is misleading because the holder continued to occupy his previous home because it was accessible to the holding.

Where the land only was acquired and made fit for the holder, but no house or buildings provided, the holdings are described as "bare land" holdings. In 70 per cent of the cases before the war the holdings were "bare". Of the holdings provided since the war 54 per cent are of this type.

The general system, so far pursued, has been to provide the holding and then leave the settler to do the best he can for himself, although in many districts the experts employed by the County Councils have given much time advising or helping the Holders. The result of this system places the small-holder at a serious disadvantage. It has meant that too high a proportion of his slender resources has been devoted to a needless duplication of working implements, to sheds and equipment of other sorts. He is always at a disadvantage in having to buy in small quantities, and worse placed than any other farmer in selling his produce, or in obtaining the best quality live-stock. This last fact is responsible for the high proportion of failures amongst small-holders who have taken up poultry keeping. They have often been the victims of the atrocious system of acquiring their stock of day-old chicks through attractively-worded advertisements without reliable guarantees, in consequence of which losses from disease or weakly stock have ruined many of them.

Apart from these drawbacks, inherent in a system which prides itself in developing individualism, the life of the Family Farmer is a very hard one. There is little doubt that the knowledge of the sort of life that must be followed by the average small-holder under the present system is the main reason why such a small proportion of experienced agricultural workers apply. They prefer regular employment under good conditions, if they can get it, to the hazards and ceaseless toil of the life of the small-holder.

The standard of life of the majority of Family Farmers is very poor. Both the farmer and his wife and, often, his family have to work all the hours of daylight and, where stock keeping is their chief occupation (as in most cases it is), week-days and Sundays all the year round, with little or no time off for any of them and only the minimum of pocket-money for the members of the family.

I question whether the standard of life for the majority is much better than that of the same classes of workers in near European countries. An enquiry in Würtemburg in 1930, where 98 per cent of the farmers are peasant proprietors, showed that most of them earned less than the average paid land worker. Nearly half the working population on the land in France is women, and more than half in Germany. The proportion is much less in this country because we have so few family farmers, but the lot of the small-holder's wife is similar here.

Many of us like to work in our gardens or on allotments in the light evenings, and often do so for long hours. But it is quite a different thing when that has to be the case all day and every day, winter and summer.

It is extraordinary that this fact of low money earnings is adopted as one of the chief reasons put forward for small-holdings by Mr. Lloyd Geroge in *How to Tackle Unemployment*. The contention was (pp. 36-7 and 42) that the payment of good wages was one of the chief reasons for the decline in British Agriculture. It was urged that

"a second cause of the difficulties of British agriculture is that the effect of this steady lowering of costs and of production abroad has been intensified since the war by the *policy deliberately adopted by the nation of not allowing the wages of agricultural labourers to fall below a minimum level*"[1] (p. 36).

In effect, therefore, this low standard of money earnings was urged as a reason for adopting "the family farm where hired labour costs are eliminated" (p. 42).

I do not believe myself that a properly managed system of small-holdings need involve this degradation of the standard of life, but it is certain that we can never establish a contented and prosperous countryside on the basis of working all the hours of daylight with nothing better than maintenance and a little pocket-money at the end of it.

Unless we can establish Land Settlement schemes that give the Settlers a life and a living comparable with that which public opinion rightly demands for the rest of the population, the system is condemned in advance.

Apart from this, in the proposals for the wholesale establishment of family farms put forward by Mr. Lloyd George, no mention was made of the people who are now getting their living off the land it was proposed to take. Land now occupied by Small-holders is of course ruled out,

[1] My italics.

and new holdings can only be established on land at present occupied by larger holdings. The records show that there are about 170,000 holdings exceeding 50 acres in extent, and the average size of these holdings is 154 acres. The average number of persons employed upon them per holding is 4·3. If, therefore, 3,000,000 acres of this land were taken, and the persons now employed upon them displaced, it involves the displacement of about 20,000 farmers and 86,000 farm workers. These people seem to have been lost sight of in Mr. Lloyd George's scheme. The most lenient thing one can say about calculations that leave out of account a social displacement of this magnitude is that they are badly in need of revision.

Let us get away from these miscalculations and consider what is practical in terms of the policy that ought to be adopted.

We must recognise that we can only check the drift from the Land if we make conditions on the countryside such as will induce young people to stay there. Not only must work be available under self-respecting conditions, but the worker must have a home, with security attached to it, that will satisfy him and his wife. Also the conditions of life in the village should be such as will make life interesting. These things must be at the back of our minds all the time and must condition the plans that are made.

We have to bear in mind also that any scheme of land settlement not only requires suitable qualification amongst those available, but is subject to the limitations of time and machinery connected with the selection and training of applicants who have not previously had suitable experience, as well as for the acquisition and equipment of the necessary land.

There is indeed no other branch of agricultural development in which the time factor is more important in limiting what you would like to do by what you can do. Mr. Lloyd George's notion that you can somehow or another select, train and settle 100,000 men in appropriate holdings on the land in from three to five years is fantastic. Perhaps

Herr Hitler, with his enormous powers and with a conscripted population, could put 100,000 men to work on the land in that time or in less, but they would not be "settled". Do let us keep in mind that what we are aiming at is the settlement of happy people who will wish to live and thrive and bring up their families in the country. This can only be done by giving the right opportunity to the right people.

How are we to find the right people, and how are we to provide the right conditions?

We may assume that the existing applicants who have been approved as suitable by County Councils have the necessary qualifications, but as soon as we get outside them we are confronted with the problems of selection and training.

In order to succeed a man must be physically fit and, either from past experience or from training, have the necessary knowledge and aptitude, but he must like the life on the land as well, and what applies to him applies with equal force to his wife.

Experience of the Land Settlement Association

During the past four years a most instructive experiment has been carried on by the Land Settlement Association, and the lessons which have emerged so far are worth noting.

In default, presumably, of making a properly planned use of their powers under the Land Utilisation Act, the Government established the Land Settlement Association to select, train and settle 2,000 men who had been previously unemployed.

Other duties have been given to the Association at different times, but we may confine ourselves to an examination of the progress made with the original plan of settlement that was initiated in 1934.

It would be difficult to imagine a harder task than that given to the Association. They were required to select men who had been unemployed for *long periods*, and who had been engaged in industrial occupations such as coal mining and ship building and who were resident in restricted "special" areas.

The Association therefore could only select from men who had had the debilitating and depressing experience of long unemployment and who, at the most, had had nothing more in the way of experience than the cultivation of an allotment or a small garden. There has never been any lack of applicants; but the process of selection has been exceedingly difficult and has provided a heart-breaking revelation of what long-continued unemployment means.

The general plan has been to acquire estates on which there could be a settlement, on an average, of about fifty settlers. In some cases, owing to the character of the the land and to the extent of the estate, a greater number than fifty may ultimately be provided for, but that has been the average size of settlement aimed at.

In the early days accommodation was provided for the selected trainees in the Farm House belonging to the estate or in improvised hostels, the land around the house being used as a Central Farm for purposes common to the undertaking—training, cultivation of breeding stock, etc., and the men worked either on the Central Farm or upon their holdings as they were gradually got ready and provided with cottages, buildings and roads.

The man undergoing training continued to receive unemployment assistance and his wife and family were maintained at home until they could be brought down to the new holding.

After the man has completed his training he still receives unemployment allowance for some months, and until the end of that time the sales from his holding are credited to his account to be used to start him as an independent settler, together with a stated amount of working capital made available through the Association.

The holdings for the most part have been either for pigs and poultry or for market gardening with some glass-house provision.

The first settlements were made on five estates in 1935; and at the present time there are some eighteen different estates to which 1,114 men have been brought down for training and possible settlement.

It would be a good thing if some of those who advised Mr. Lloyd George that this was a short cut to remedy unemployment would make themselves acquainted at first hand with the realities that have been experienced. It is true, as I have said, that the Association were given a task of superlative difficulty in that they could only take men from limited areas from other occupations and who had also been unemployed for a long time, and no rational scheme to promote Land Settlement, as such, would be accompanied by these artificial and onerous restrictions. These conditions have added enormously to the cost and made the task of administration immensely more difficult, but they have provided some exceedingly useful experience which, with proper adjustments, might be made good use of.

A large proportion of the men when they arrived on the estates displayed, through the sufferings of long-continued unemployment, a very depressed standard of physical and mental vigour. It is fair to say that, with many of them, it required from six to nine months good feeding and careful training before they could do a day's work, as ordinarily understood by men accustomed to the occupation.

Up to the end of December 1937, 371 men out of the 1,114 for various reasons had returned to their former districts. In some cases because they had an opportunity of resuming their old occupation, but in the majority of cases because they, or their wives, did not like the work and life, or were not suitable for it.

It appears certain that nearly all the men who have now become settled are likely to make good. Some of them already are doing very well. The results show that a good man, on a good holding, can make a living, but there is no such person as an "average" man. For instance, on one estate, amongst men working on the same-sized holdings under identical conditions, one man realised a net profit during his period of training of £300, whilst another man, who started at the same time and had carried on under precisely the same conditions, had only £64 to his credit.

In some cases, particularly in poultry, owing to the need for obtaining large quantities of young stock quickly, the results have been disastrous mainly because of the lack of stamina of the poultry obtained in that way, and the Association has been compelled to make its own arrangements on central farms for raising its own stock.

Substantially it amounts to this; about two-thirds of those who have been accepted for training by the Association are likely to become permanent tenants of the Association and self-supporting citizens in their new occupation.

The system developed by the Association differs very widely from that adopted by County Councils. It represents a grouped settlement system under which, whilst each settler does the best he can for himself he has the support of a large-scale organisation in many essential services.

A Warden employed by the Association is in charge of each estate. It is his business to give guidance in planning the cultivation programme, to help in the provision of livestock and to be responsible for the arrangements for the orderly assembly, packing, grading and transport of produce. Behind the wardens are Specialists employed by the Association whose business it is to advise and help settlers in regard to Market Gardening, Poultry husbandry, or Pig rearing, as the case may be. In addition, arrangements are made for the provision of packing material and other requirements, and for gradually improving the standardisation and marketing of the different products.

Beyond this a Central Committee of the Association purchases feeding-stuffs, seeds and fertilisers, in bulk, for all the different estates, and the advantage of the lower prices thus obtained are passed on to the settlers. A system has also been developed for planning the lay-out of the Estates in such a way that ploughing and other operations may be done on a large scale through machinery kept on the central farms.

Some two years ago, in company with my friend Mr. George Dallas, I was appointed to the Executive of the Association and I have had the advantage, on this and on other Committees, of first-hand acquaintance with the difficulties that have been experienced and of the arrangements that have been adopted in the development of this novel experiment.

I think it can fairly be said, to quote from a recent report, that "the experience of the Association is now long enough to justify its belief that under this system a man who has the aptitude and the necessary physical strength, should be able to earn a reasonable living and also enjoy a good life".

The concluding words of this quotation refer to the activities that are gradually springing up in the older Settlements where life has become regularised, whereby the Settlers are combining to provide the amenities and opportunities for enjoyment and recreation which people ought to have and which most of them perhaps did have in various ways before they fell out of work.

The experiment is a costly one. Including the provision of a house and necessary buildings and equipment for the holdings, road-making, drainage, layout and provision of working capital in livestock and otherwise to enable a start to be made, the cost exceeds £1,000 per settler.

In considering this enterprise we have necessarily to make many allowances for its special character, but there is no doubt that if the approved applicants at present on County Registers could have a system of holding which would provide them with the immense advantages which the Association holders are provided with, as compared with the ordinary Smallholder who is left on his own, they would jump at the opportunity.

So far as small-holdings should be promoted as a part of the scheme of increased cultivation I am considering in this chapter, there is no doubt that grouped settlements, that have the advantage of good scientific direction and skilled assistance in mechanical services, in buying and selling, offer a much more promising way of developing land settlement than the methods that had been pursued hitherto.

Alternative Methods

The Small-holding method in one form or another does not, however, exhaust the possibilities of encouraging intensive cultivation, particularly where market gardening, glasshouse production and fruit-growing are concerned.

I have become convinced that it is not, in fact, the easiest and most promising method, although sound National policy should provide for its development on the grouped small-holding colony system under unified direction where the land was appropriate.

Many large farms are at present being used to develop market-garden production on a scale big enough to make proper provision for skilled direction and management, and I have been given the opportunity of examining some of them.

Fordson Estates Ltd.

One of the most promising is that being made on the Fordson Estates Ltd., at Boreham near Chelmsford, and I am indebted to Lord Perry and his colleagues for full particulars of their operations and for getting out the figures I shall quote.

The whole estate is about 3,000 acres and is divided into a number of units. The charges for management, maintenance, repairs, transport, marketing, book-keeping and the rest, are distributed over the different units on a proportionate basis.

The three largest units contain about 400, 600 and 800 acres of land respectively, including woodlands and waste ground. These three farms have been formed into separate Co-operative Societies under the Industrial and Provident Societies Acts. The accounts of each are kept separately and each make their contribution *pro rata* to the common estate charges.

It is sufficient to confine this examination to these cases

although the rest of the Estate is managed similarly, though not in the form of a Co-operative Society.

Before they were purchased in 1931 these three farms consisted of seven separate tenancies which employed in all 47 men on mixed and Dairy farming—an average employment of 2·6 men per hundred acres of used land.

The existing scheme was started in 1934 after the estate had been put in order, fences removed, etc., and the figures supplied to me comprise the four working years. At the present time 87 men, excluding those engaged on services common to the whole estate, are permanently employed on the same farms, giving an average of 4·8 per hundred acres. If we deduct the woodlands and other unused land, as has been done for the previous farms, the calculation is 6·7 men per hundred acres of land actually cultivated. The number of extraneous employees which should be added to these in respect of office, transport, etc., is sixteen, so that the land is now supporting about 8 men per hundred acres.

The wages formerly paid were at the County rate of 30s. a week.

The wages now paid are the County rate, plus 23 per cent. The County rate was raised in 1937 to 32s. 6d. and the rate of wages therefore now averages 40s. per week. If, however, the profits exceed the payment of 4 per cent, free of tax, on capital, and the other charges that I will describe, they are distributed in the form of a bonus at the end of a year, proportional to earnings.

In 1935 one of the farms made no profit available for distribution and in 1936 no bonus was distributed on two of the farms. One of them just paid its way and the other had a substantial loss owing to the bad weather and poor prices. With these exceptions, however, bonuses have been paid each year of varying amounts, and the amounts for 1937 are shown in the detailed accounts which will be given later.

There is central direction in management, and there are three separate departments for Transport; for Building, for Repairs; and for Office work. The charges for the Transport Department are made on the standard of competitive prices. The charges for the Repairs, Maintenance and Mechanics section are charged at cost, plus 25 per cent for labour and 15 per cent on material. The Office section has been financed by charges of 5 per cent commission on purchases and $2\frac{1}{2}$ per cent commission on sales.

Each of these Sections has been worked on a separate basis for three years only. The realised net profit up to date for the Transport section is £499; the Building and Mechanics Section £379; and the Office section £223.

At my request a detailed analysis was made of the difference in cost obtained by centralised purchase as compared with current market prices for all the purchases during a year on the largest farm unit of 800 acres. The result showed that the savings effected on total purchases of £5,089 3s. 6d. amounted to £740 2s. 8d. which meant that about £490 was returned for the benefit of the farm account, after the £250 (or 5 per cent on £5,000) had been taken for office costs. It is evident, however, that by being able to operate through a large firm like Messrs. Ford, more advantageous terms might have been obtained for such supplies as petrol, oil and other items, and these advantages were expressly excluded from the figure given.

Tractors are depreciated at the rate of $22\frac{1}{2}$ per cent, general farm implements at 10 per cent plus 1–10 per cent, and the rate of interest charged on the Capital provided is 4 per cent free of tax.

The actual capital expenditure for land improvement in various forms on the whole estate to the end of 1937 was £8,560 and a further reserve of £7,636 has been set aside, averaging in all a little less than £7 10s. per acre. This is probably a smaller figure than might be required on much land although a good deal of the land was in a bad condition.

Lord Perry tells me that as the result of their experience he thinks that the unit of foreman-management should be about 300 acres, and that in order to cover the proper charges for management and for implements so as to secure the fullest use of implements, the size of the whole estate should not be less than 3,000 acres.

The Produce of the three sections of the estate that I am describing during 1936-7 was as follows:—

No. 1		No. 2		No. 3	
Wheat	. 14%	Wheat	. 9%	Wheat	. 14%
Peas and		Peas and		Peas and	
Beans	. 37%	Beans	. 32%	Beans	. 38%
Cabbage and		Cabbage and		Cabbage and	
Cauliflower	16%	Cauliflower	20%	Cauliflower	22%
Sprouts	. 24%	Sprouts	. 23%	Sprouts	. 21%
Potatoes	. 5%	Sundries	. 5%	Potatoes	. 1%
Sundries	. 4%	Asparagus .	7%	Sundries	. 4%
		Lettuce	. 4%		

The average of the sales and expenses of the three estates for four years up to the end of 1937 is set out in the accompanying table.

The figures of the "*Average Cost per Acre*" include wages, seeds, packages, manures, transport charges, implement depreciation and repairs and all other working expenses.

The costs of Management include all office charges as well as building repairs and all estate maintenance work.

The loss on Number 3 is accounted for by the serious loss already referred to that was experienced in 1936.

1934–1937

Farm	Average Sales per acre £ s. d.			Average Cost per acre £ s. d.			Average Management per acre £ s. d.		
No. 1	17	0	8	15	8	1	1	3	1
No. 2	21	11	1	17	14	8	1	5	0
No. 3	18	2	8	17	12	8	1	0	6

It was interesting to find that the expenditure on artificial manure as well as on Labour was greatest on Farm No. 2, which showed the best profit per acre.

R₂

The following is a complete summary of the different transactions on the three farms for the last completed year:—

	No. 1			No. 2			No. 3		
	£	s.	d.	£	s.	d.	£	s.	d.
Sales	7,878	1	10	13,490	0	7	17,309	2	7
Costs	6,840	14	7	11,760	14	10	15,743	8	3
Management expenses	578	3	6	769	17	2	965	3	8
Working Profit	460	3	9	959	8	7	600	10	8
less Interest Charges	180	7	6	277	16	3	410	14	6
Net Profit	279	16	3	681	12	4	189	16	2

It should be added in conclusion that since 1934 in addition to full-time workers' wages and bonuses, payments have been made for casual labour, including picking, exceeding £17,000 for the three farms together.

I have quoted this case in detail because it shows very clearly what can be done on moderate land with skilled management combined with adequate capital.

The arrangements for the sale of market-garden produce, as we have already seen, are deplorable at present and producers' prices are low out of all reason compared with what the consumer pays, but by the increased production that has resulted from a fuller use of the land in this case it has been possible to give whole-time employment to twice the number of men previously employed on the same land and to pay them an average wage of 40s. a week apart from any extras in the way of bonuses, and apart from substantial sums paid for casual labour.

The procedure that has been adopted is to have frequent consultation amongst the management to plan the cropping, cultural and mechanical operations, to spend freely on fertilisers and manures, to grade as far as possible in accordance with the requirements of the market and to plan packing, assembly and the use of transport in a well-thought-out and systematic way.

All this, of course, is only possible if these four essentials are brought together: adequate capital—good management and the use of scientific methods—a sufficient area of land to bear the costs of administration—and, finally, accurate accounting.

Fruit Production

It is not necessary to extend this examination to the case of fruit production. I find exactly the same results follow for fruit production as for market-garden produce when similar methods are applied.

Many cases could be quoted to show that the advantages are indeed somewhat more easily obtainable where science and good management are applied, with adequate capital, to fruit production, especially for good dessert apples. The planning of the orchards, the use of intermediate land, spraying, pruning, grading, packing, storage and the other operations lend themselves more easily to producing good results than the more varied operations attached to the cultivation of diverse vegetable crops, but the principles are the same and the case need not be elaborated.

Existing marketing arrangements for fruit, except in times of scarcity through frost or other similar causes, are, if possible, worse than for vegetables. A bumper crop is nearly always bad for the grower and at such times it is common enough for beautiful plums to be left on the ground to rot, or to be sold for little more than the cost of picking. There is no branch of production in which it is more important that the creation of a good sales organisation, with adequate storage accommodation and other associated facilities, should go hand in hand with the extension of cultivation. It would be the business of the National Commission to see that they did.

Conclusion

This chapter has, necessarily, been longer than others, but it has dealt with complicated and controversial questions.

To sum it up in the terms of the Programme already formulated. We need an additional 400,000 acres for fruit and vegetable requirements. Special attention should be devoted to the cultivation of the orchard and small fruits that we can produce so well and now import in such large quantities.

The policy that I suggest should be:—

1. To promote large-scale farming organisations, as outlined in the previous chapter, for the purpose of the amalgamation of suitable land, as it can be set free, in units of not less than 3,000 acres with market-garden produce as the main crops associated with the development of canning for appropriate commodities.

2. The units of area for fruit production would be smaller. An area of 500 acres according to the district is probably large enough.

3. Coincidentally with this, Small-holdings should be developed in selected districts for men who are capable and experienced, or who may have become so after training. In any case the present system of leaving the small-holder helpless on his own should be abandoned. A grouped system should be adopted and the land occupied by the group should be extensive enough to bear the costs of experienced management in sales, purchases, storage and marketing, together with the provision of mechanical assistance common to the enterprise so far as practicable.

Experience will show which system yields the best results in production and in satisfaction of life. My belief is that the first method will be found preferable except in a few areas where the most intensive forms of production may be suitable.

In any case the plans of the National Commission will be limited for some time to come by the extent to which they can bring men into the industry and make good our deplorable loss of splendid labourers.

PART III

SECTION V

Chapter XIX

Reclamation—Afforestation—Amenities

Reclamation

RECLAMATION, OR THE bringing of waste land into cultivation, has practically ceased in Great Britain since 1892. Up to that time the process was always going on to some extent, and there is much more land that would be worth reclamation than is commonly supposed; but the neglect of it has been part and parcel of our general attitude and lack of land policy. The usual comment whenever the subject has been mentioned in Parliament has been to the effect: "If we can't get a living off the land that has been reclaimed, why bother about reclaiming any more."

There is a good deal of justice in that comment; especially in the absence of any sense of national responsibility in the matter, but it does not prove that reclamation would not be worth while if it were tackled properly. As a matter of fact it would be in many places, but it has been nobody's business, so nothing has been done. On the contrary the reverse process has been in operation and much land has been let slip back into the wild.

In *Agriculture After the War*,[1] Sir Daniel Hall reports on five different types of lands in Great Britain where reclamation should be undertaken. He makes the work,

[1] Loc. cit., pp. 70–82.

however, to be conditional upon its being done with the same careful regard to the character of the soil and its chemical needs as has been displayed in the extensive reclamation works that have been carried out successfully in Germany, as well as in Holland, Belgium and other countries. There are considerable stretches of good land waiting for embankment and drainage along the Wash, and smaller amounts in the estuary of the Dee, in the Firth of Forth and elsewhere, but uncertainty of title appears to have been an obstacle in many cases where the land would obviously be worth the expenditure. National ownership would remove that obstacle.

The largest expanses of land in this country which Sir Daniel Hall suggests as worth reclaiming are the "brek", or sandy heath, lands in Norfolk and Suffolk, in some parts of Surrey, Sussex, Hampshire and Dorset. Large stretches of similar lands have, he says, been advantageously reclaimed in Germany at a cost of from £5 to £6 an acre, and he quotes a successful experiment of the Development Commission in Norfolk as illustrating the possibilities on this type of soil.

There is no necessity for me to elaborate the details.[1] We cannot expect anything to be done, even when the work would be well justified, until we get a rational Agricultural system and have a National Authority in existence competent to deal with it.

The value of the work in times of serious unemployment is obvious. The National Commission, under the plans I am advocating, would have its hands full for a long time, but we cannot imagine its neglecting the preparation of plans for the valuable works of reclamation that would be awaiting its enterprises.

Afforestation

Up to this point we have been considering the use of Land for Food Production, for arresting the tragic shrinkage

[1] Readers who are interested are advised to read Sir Daniel Hall's Chapter on this subject.

of that which is described as "cultivated" and for adding to it some part of the rough "grazings."

But this is far from accounting for all the land. There are fifty-six million acres in Great Britain, apart from Lakes and Water, so that there is a balance of twenty-six million acres of one sort of another beyond the present cultivated area.

Big as our cities and towns are, they do not occupy much more than about four million acres even when we have made allowance for all the straggling tentacles of rows of houses that ribbon development has pushed out into the fields.

The unaccounted area still remaining contains fifteen million acres of grazing of various degrees of "roughness" and the rest is not by any means all mountain tops or bog, or useless waste. Nearly three million acres of it are described as Private Woodland. A part of it is well-timbered, or was felled during the war and is still rough and un-planted; a great extent consists of coppices, scrub and other woodland of no commercial value.

The Forestry Committee of 1918 reported on the waste lands generally and, after excluding all those parts which for one reason or another should be left out of account, came to the conclusion[1] that there were from four to five million acres that should be afforested.

The results of the Report of this Committee have been very important. It led to the establishment in 1919 of the present Forestry Commission and to the formation of our first considered programme of afforestation. The Com-mittee of 1918 is usually, and deservedly, known as the Acland Committee from the fact that Sir F. R. Acland, Bt., M.P., was its Chairman.

The Acland Programme had as its objective the removal of our excessive dependence upon supplies of imported timber during war-time and, for that purpose, planned afforestation that would yield a three years' supply on the basis of an annual importation of ten million loads of timber.

[1] First Report of the Forestry Sub-Committee of the Reconstruction Committee, 1918, cmd. 8881, p. 37.

Their programme, therefore, did not provide for the afforestation of more than half the land which they regarded as worth planting; but, with this three years' supply as their limited objective, they proposed that the three million acres of private woodlands should be brought into proper order and a national afforestation authority be made responsible for planting a further 1,180,000 acres of conifers during the first forty years, and completing 1,770,000 acres at the end of eighty years, with a smaller area of hardwoods.

The Forestry Commission was established in 1919 so that we are now in a position to speak with more confidence.

In January 1938 Sir Roy Robinson, the Chairman of the Commission, reviewed the position in an address to the Chartered Surveyors' Institution[1] and those who need a little strengthening of their faith in the case for the national ownership of the Land are advised to read his address, although, as an intensely practical public servant, Sir Roy Robinson was concerned only with the great job of work of which he has charge and not with political considerations.

He reported that the experience of the Commission justified the conclusion he had placed before the Estimates Committee of the House of Commons[2] that

"If all the relevant expenditure be charged, the probable yield on afforestation with conifers, which constitute some 90 per cent of the total plantings, will be between 3 per cent and $3\frac{1}{2}$ per cent. The yield on deciduous trees is lower."

It appears also from his address to the Surveyors that the estimate of the Acland Committee that from four to five million acres was the area of properly plantable land, may prove to be an underestimate. He says:—

"I believe that we are well on the way towards proving that many hundreds of thousands of acres of practically worthless land hitherto classified as unplantable, can be successfully afforested at low cost."[3]

[1] See the Journal of the Chartered Surveyors' Institution, January and February 1938.
[2] Report of the Estimates Committee with Evidence, 1937, No. 86 143.
[3] Loc. cit., pp. 80–1. January number.

The experience of the Commission has shown that our natural advantages in timber production are greater than many have suspected. Sir R. Robinson tells us that we can grow no less than 90 per cent of our present imports of timber in good *quality*. The red and white woods of northern Europe are the products of the Scots Pine and the Norway Spruce, and the Oregon Pine is identical with our Douglas Fir. Our hardwoods of Oak, Ash, Beech and Sycamore also are second to none.

We can produce good *quantity* also. Some of the trees are found to grow more quickly here than in the countries from which they are now imported. The British market, as in the case with Food, is the best of all.

Those who know the Chairman of the Forestry Commission are aware that he is a cautious man, and his forecast of a yield to the nation of from 3 to $3\frac{1}{2}$ per cent in the afforestation of an immense extent of land not now included in any programme, is a fact of great national importance. It has brought into the realm of certainty what was hopeful anticipation with the Acland Committee. It is a splendid thing to be assured that instead of the half measures—or rather, safety measures—to which we are at present committed, we are justified in proposing the afforestation of a possible $4\frac{1}{2}$ million acres of land in addition to existing private woodlands.

The amount of employment that forestry work provides is less than many suppose, but it would be difficult to over-estimate the restoration and employment that would be afforded in the course of time as the trees came to maturity and the many industries came into being which are associated with timber utilisation. It would lead also to the establishment of community life once more in many places that have been allowed to become desolate.

Later on I will try and estimate what the results would be in terms of employment, but our programme should be to arrange for the ultimate planting of all the land that can profitably be afforested. It comprises more than twice the area involved in the existing programme.

We shall better appreciate what such a programme would require, and the mistakes that should be avoided in undertaking it, if we recall some of the experiences of the present Forestry Commission.

The Programme of the Acland Committee was that 250,000 acres should be planted in the first decade, at the end of which time the annual planting should have reached 30,000 acres a year; and that it should be continued at an annual average of 34,300 acres. The planting during the first ten years was to consist of 150,000 acres by the Commission and the balance by restoring private woodlands and by planting assisted, jointly, by the Commission, Local Authorities and private owners. It was proposed also that at the end of ten years 400,000 acres of land should have been acquired by the Commission.

The results, in fact, at the end of the first ten-year period were that the work on private woodlands was far behind. The planting by the Commission was only 19,000 acres behind the programme and the annual planting had reached a 25,000-acre level, but the land acquisition was 90,000 acres short.

To some extent the arrears were due to the difficulties inevitably experienced at the end of the war in starting a new enterprise, in getting together skilled personnel and in training forest officers, but chiefly to the crazy action of the Geddes Economy Committee in 1922 in cutting down the grants so soon after the commencement of the work and thereby crippling progress for three years.

The Commission had recovered from this by 1931, when there was a repetition of "Economy" cuts. A little explanation will suffice to show how far-reaching are the effects of such interruptions in work of this kind.

The young trees are three years old when planted and, allowing for a previous season in the preparation of the ground, the work must be four years in advance of actual planting. When the cuts were made in 1931 the Commission found itself in possession of millions of young trees ready for planting which they were not allowed to plant, as well as millions more coming behind which there would not be land enough for. It was therefore compelled to make its contributions to "National Economy" by slowing down the acquisition and preparation of land, and by actually burning many millions of seedlings that it had carefully raised.

The resulting diminution of planting continued until 1936, when it had fallen to 20,576 acres.

In 1935 the grants were restored and the Commission was instructed to prepare for an annual planting of 30,000 acres. Under this scheme planting is expected to reach 24,000 acres during the present year and, if we are spared a repetition of folly masquerading as economy, the full acreage will soon be obtained.

The position now is that the Commission is the largest single landowner in the country and has acquired a million acres of land of which 620,000 acres are plantable and 310,000 acres have been planted. The remainder of the land (nearly 400,000 acres) consists of 30,000 acres that have been let in 680 small-holdings, 12,000 acres that have been similarly let to forest workers, and some 350,000 acres of miscellaneous and unplantable land that was necessarily acquired in the purchase of different estates.

It was to have been expected that, as their work extended, the Commission would experience more and more difficulty in obtaining land. This promises to be the delaying factor in the programme of expansion.

What has been said of Nursery work indicates only one of the steps that must be taken well in advance in a programme of work that must be long-term in character.

Land must be obtained in advance of planting in accordance with the quantities and types of seedlings destined for it. It must be cleared of scrub and rubbish, the rabbits got rid of, and fencing and other preparatory work completed.

At the same time more labour must be obtained and trained, additional forest officers brought into the work, and housing and other accommodation got ready for those who will be engaged in preparation of the ground, fencing and planting.

None of these things are difficult in themselves; but they show how essential it is that forestry work should be planned well ahead and continuously sustained without a haunting fear of some new Geddes Axe or another.

Before trying to express the possibilities now established in terms of an amended planting programme, reference should be made to the three million acres of private woodlands. These woodlands have been carefully surveyed and should provide not only the most accessible, but the most substantial, first contribution to forestry development. Progress upon them has been lamentable.

About a million and a half acres of what are described as "reasonably productive" woods survived the war. During the war 478,000 acres were felled and the annual Report of the Commission for 1934 said that

> "on the most favourable estimates not more than 80,000 acres of lee-way have been made up, leaving still unplanted some 400,000 acres of felled and devastated woodland. In other words it is more than doubtful whether any real progress has been made in maintaining the existing woodlands on even the relatively low pre-war standard."[1]

In addition to this area of felled woodland there are coppices which represent "under modern conditions a poor form of silviculture"[2] and half a million acres of scrub or amenity woods either producing nothing or of little value.

The planting grants that have been made since 1919 have resulted in the planting of 115,000 acres, but Sir Roy Robinson's conclusion after this "cold comfort" is that apart from the planting or replanting "it is doubtful whether the remainder of the private woodlands—that is to say, the bulk of the area—is in as good a condition, silviculturally, as it was in 1919".[3]

The explanation for this state of affairs is twofold—economic and personal. As to the economic, woods have

---

[1] The Fifteenth Annual Report (H.C. 76).
[2] Address to the Surveyors' Institution, p. 70.
[3] Loc. cit., pp. 75-6.

often been felled because "the owners needed cash, and neglected for the same reasons" because of high taxation, death duties or for other causes. On the personal side, many owners, we are told, "are indifferent so long as the woods provide a cover for game or are ornamental"; others regard forestry as a poor form of investment (which for the lifetime of a single individual, it is) or "just don't care whether their woods contribute anything towards the well-being or safety of the nation".[1]

There is nothing surprising in any of this. It is the same story as with agricultural land generally, and for my part I cannot feel much disposition to blame owners. A forest only begins to yield its harvest in any substantial form after forty years have elapsed, and it is not in full bearing in valuable timber until eighty years or so. The great timber supplies that the world is now using up so fast were not planted by man—they are the fruits of nature. It is our duty to safeguard the future in our own land so far as we can, but we cannot expect private citizens to provide for posterity here any more than in any other country. It is the duty of the State in Britain just as it is being recognised as such in other countries.

With regard to what action is required, the Chairman of the Commission says that, except for the manifestly small proportion of owners who want to improve their woodlands and have not the means to do so, he sees no course open except some scheme of "joint ownership with some measure of State Control in management" or "compulsion"; for, as he justly concludes,[2] "the development of the modern State is towards more direct control of the use to which land is put".

This is in complete accord with the general thesis of this book as regards food production. It is evident that, with timber as with food, we can never secure the best use of the land unless it is nationally owned and unless it is accepted as a national responsibility that a well directed and sustained effort should be made to secure its proper use.

The time has therefore come when we should have a

[1] Address to the Surveyors' Institution, p. 76.   [2] Loc. cit., p. 83.

forestry programme that is based on the afforestation of land that is appropriate to that purpose rather than the minor project of having sufficient timber to supply the nation for three years in the event of war.

In connection with such a programme it should be observed that our imports have increased by two million loads per annum since the Acland Committee made their calculations. This is mainly due to the increased uses to which wood pulp is devoted. On the basis of an import of twelve million loads, the Chairman calculates that our home annual production of mature timber could ultimately be worked up to an amount that would yield *each year* from 30 to 40 per cent of our present imports of unmanufactured timber, or between 20 and 30 per cent of the total consumption, including wood pulp.

This would mean that the planting programme would have to be worked up to an annual average of 40,000 acres. We are told that such a programme possesses "no inherent difficulties provided the land can be obtained well in advance, and that is the obstacle on which a large scheme would be most likely to come to grief".[1]

Now, let me estimate so far as I can what such a forestry programme might mean in terms of employment.

The cleaning of the ground, the clearance of rabbits, fencing and planting provide much work, particularly during the winter season. After this there is a period of from fifteen to twenty years, until thinnings begin, during which maintenance can be provided by a small amount of resident labour.

This maintenance work is mainly provided by those who occupy "forest holdings". The holdings consist of a cottage and a small acreage of land that can be worked by the resident holder when he is not employed on the plantations. The holdings provided by the Commission contain an average of about eleven acres each and the production of milk and the raising of stock, pigs and poultry are the chief occupations of the holders.

[1] Address to the Surveyors' Institution, p. 82.

Up to the end of 1936 the Commission had established 1,268 holdings on its planted area of 310,000 acres, or about four holdings per thousand acres. During 1936 the Commission was asked by the Government to arrange for the afforestation of 200,000 acres in the special areas of South Wales, Durham, Northumberland and West Cumberland in connection with which they were to provide a thousand Forest holdings. This represents five holdings per thousand acres, but it will be safe to take four per thousand as an average figure applicable to a complete national scheme.

In addition to the planting and maintenance workers, there are the Central, Scientific and Nursery staffs, which although they would increase as the work proceeded, would not be added to in the same proportions as the increase of the planted area because they are largely associated with the annual planting work which would remain at a steady figure of between forty and fifty thousand acres.

The total employment afforded by the Commission on 310,000 planted acres in 1936 (of which 20,576 were planted during the year) was a maximum during the winter of 4,565 men and a minimum of 3,720 during the summer, including the 1,268 forest holders.

The Acland Committee allowed for the employment of ten men per hundred acres of annual planting, but the numbers employed by the Commission appear to be substantially more than that.

In accordance, however, with the practice previously adopted in estimating labour requirements I will take the lower estimate of the Acland Committee and thereby make some allowance for a possible increase in the use of mechanical appliances.

The following quotation from the Acland Report gives an excellent picture of the development of employment in connection with Forestry work after plantations are made:—

"Apart from the cleaning which the young trees require for two or three years after planting and occasional repairs to fences and drains, plantations need little attention until about the fifteenth year, when quick-growing species may require a light thinning. From that time onwards the amount of labour employed will increase steadily as the plantations have to be thinned a second and a third time. The preparation of the thinnings for pit-props, roadmaking and the haulage of the material to rail will all absorb increasing amounts of labour. By the twenty-fifth year all these operations together with planting operations should be proceeding. By the fortieth year it may be found advisable to begin on a small scale the clear felling of the first-planted areas. Timber large enough for sawing should begin to be produced about the fiftieth year, and by the eightieth year the forest should be in full working order. It will then require about one man per hundred acres for felling, replanting, repairs to roads and miscellaneous work not including the conversion of the timber. The last-named operation should give employment to about the same number of men as the forest work itself".[1]

On this basis of one man per hundred acres on forest work and one other man per hundred acres on timber conversion, the Acland Committee estimated that the labour ultimately required on the 1,770,000 acres of forest would be 33,000 men, out of which they thought that 25,000 might be regarded as permanent settlers engaged in the new industry.

This estimate was apart from the labour that would be needed for the restoration and use of private woodlands—the area of which, if we exclude all that is already fairly well grown, is not less than 1,500,000 acres. Some labour is already employed on this ground as gamekeepers or woodmen, although much less than a full forestry scheme would call for—Parenthetically it may be mentioned that Sir Roy Robinson does not think that Forestry need exclude gamekeeping in appropriate districts, but we may leave experience to devise any adjustments that may be called for

[1] Report of the Acland Committee, p. 49.

in that respect. It will be on the safe side if we reckon that in the proper afforestation of this area of derelict private woodlands there would be continuous additional work for one man only per hundred acres, or 15,000 in all.

The programme we are considering, however, contemplates the afforestation, apart from private woods, of 4½ million acres instead of the 1,770,000 acres proposed by the Acland Committee. If we apply to this larger area the estimate of the Acland Committee, employment for 70,000 men is a conservative estimate and makes a substantial allowance for reductions obtained on larger scale operations.

This figure, with the 15,000 for private woodlands, gives a total of 85,000 workers, practically all of whom, in the course of time, would be permanently employed in the forest areas.

This permanent employment would only be gradually reached as afforestation proceeded but it should be remembered that the first plantations of the Commission are already fifteen years old and are beginning to provide work in thinnings, and that various woodland industries are already springing up in connection with them in some places.

In whatever way we examine this case, it is difficult to imagine one that calls more definitely for sustained national effort than afforestation. We may be certain that in no other way can we realise the capacities for useful production of these great tracts of land.

The State can take long views. Its efforts can continue from generation to generation. It can afford to wait in providing for its future needs, whilst its citizens, with their shorter span of life, cannot do so.

We have only to visit these possible future forest lands to realise that the work of restoration will not only provide a home and healthy employment to increasing numbers of people, but that their lot will often be cast in beautiful places. Indeed the thought of what can be done fills one almost, with a feeling of envy of those who in time to come will live there.

National Parks—Preservation of Beauty—Access for Enjoyment

The increasing possession by the Forestry Commission of large areas of land, many of which are in places of exceptional beauty and are popular with those who love to explore their homeland, has made some sort of action possible, whilst the cry of expostulation at the desecration of much of the countryside has continued in helpless but growing volume.

Here again reference to past history may help us to understand the action that should be taken if the process of desecration is to be arrested and if the possibility of enjoyment of these lovely districts is to be opened to the people under proper conditions.

On September 26th, 1929, the Prime Minister (Mr. Ramsay MacDonald) appointed a Committee to report on the subject of National Parks and it so happened that I myself was the Chairman.

The Committee reported in April 1931 and stressed the necessity for action on the lines of its recommendations in the following terms:—

> "We desire to record our conviction that such measures as we have advocated are necessary if the present generation is to escape the charge that in a short-sighted pursuit of its immediate ends it has squandered a noble heritage."[1]

The urgency was stressed because of the failure of the planning machinery which existed at that time to control the rapid urbanisation that was taking place, or to check the spoliation of choice places in response to the use of them that modern transport has made possible.

The case is much worse now than in 1931, but there is no necessity to enlarge upon what has already been said,[2] except to express the hope that Mr. Clough Williams Ellis and his friends will keep up the pressure.

[1] Report of the Committee on National Parks, p. 43, Cmd 3851, 1931.
[2] Chapter IX. pp. 115–117.

The recommendations of the 1931 Committee suffered eclipse in the Economy Campaign and we have been marking time ever since, whilst the "developer" has been busy.

The proposals of the Committee are as applicable now as in 1931, except that a system of National Land ownership would make them much easier to work and the recent action of the Forestry Commission calls for some modifications of the procedure suggested by the Committee.

The Committee was emphatic that adequate planning and the efficient safeguarding of national treasures could not be left to local initiative. They concluded that there was no way of dealing with all that was required except by a National Authority with suitable powers.

It was suggested that there should be two Authorities, one for England and Wales, and one for Scotland, with a joint Board on matters of Common Policy and action.

The Authority would be required to select National Reserve Areas which would either be dealt with under a comprehensive planning scheme or preserved in their existing state until planning became called for.

It was to be the duty of the National Authority, in concert with Regional Planning Authorities, to see that plans were made for each reserved area, according to which (and only according to which) development could proceed.

The root cause of the ineffectiveness of such plans as are proposed at present, by those authorities that are sufficiently enterprising to make plans at all, is that, owing to possible claims for compensation, procedure is so beset with Notices, Hearings, and Appeals on all sorts of grounds that progress is practically impossible. Alongside this, a multiplicity of authorities—some willing, some less willing—have to be induced to co-operate, and negotiations and postponements continue year after year.

There have, for example, been proposals for years past for a plan to safeguard the entire Lake District. It is urgently needed. But a combination of the causes just referred to leaves us still without one.

The Committee of 1931 was not in a position, even if it had been willing, to devise a scheme of national land ownership, although, so far as the specially reserved areas were concerned, its proposals would have resulted in something not far short of it. There cannot be any doubt that two-thirds of the difficulties would be removed in advance if land were nationally owned.

In connection with planning, the Committee advised that there should be a single Planning Authority for the whole of each National Reserve Area. They refrained from naming the areas they thought should be scheduled because, in advance of legislation, they did not want to play into the hands of those undesirables (of whom there are always some to be found) who would buy land in advance so as to claim compensation afterwards. It does not, however, need much foresight to imagine that such areas as the Lake District, The Peak, Dovedale, Snowdonia. the New Forest, the Forest of Dean, Cannock Chase, the Gower Peninsular, Ardgoil, the Caingorm area and others like them, would have to be safeguarded.

It would also be the business of the National Authority to provide experts in Planning and to assist the Regional Authorities in other ways.

The preparation of a list of places of special charm, and still unspoilt, would be another duty of the Authority that would be exercised at the start. Many of these places are preserved now because of their relative inaccessibility but some of them would be made more accessible by suitable tracks. Meantime the fact of their being scheduled would safeguard them until a plan became required, if ever it did.

Another duty proposed by the Committee for the National Authority was the marking of footpaths and the making of Regulations and By-laws relating to the use of the areas, and for securing good behaviour.

There are many responsible and well-managed Associations of Ramblers, Camping Clubs, Scouts, Guides and others, and it was proposed to secure their co-operation as much as possible, and to provide huts, hostels, lists of cottages and other arrangements for accommodation in concert with them or, if necessary, independently.

Another duty of the National Authority would be the safeguarding of selected Sanctuaries for birds, flowers and plants. Here again, as far as possible, in association with responsible societies. The records of the spoilation that has occurred in some places by the clearance of choice flowers and plants and the destruction of rare birds were indeed shocking, and a National Authority of the kind contemplated would be the first step towards their preservation.

It is clear to me also that we can never expect to obtain the hearty public co-operation that ought to be secured in checking the depredations of the barbarians who strew lovely places with sardine tins, banana skins, broken bottles and the like, unless it can be made plain that the preservation of these beautiful places is the duty of us all and that in participating in their preservation we are safeguarding our own possessions.

I must mention, in passing, one set of facts that came out during our enquiry with regard to Deer Forests. It is sometimes urged that Deer Forest rents would make land costly to buy if compensation were made on that account; but if we want an instance of the sacrifice of human enjoyment on a large scale to the interests of sport on flimsy pretences, here is one. The average basis of valuation for Deer Forest rents is £20 per stag. The acreage for each stag is 588 acres in Aberdeenshire, 480 in Inverness, 450 to 500 in Sutherlandshire and 740 in the Black Mountain, Argyll. The rent paid, therefore, in one of the costliest of these districts (Inverness) for these purposes is 10d. per acre. That is the price of the exclusion of the sons of men in the interests of shooting a single quadruped!

There has been an interesting development during the past three years in connection with the unplantable land that has been purchased sometimes by the Forestry Commission in acquiring estates. In 1935 a Committee was appointed to

278 A PROGRAMME OF DEVELOPMENT

advise the Commission as to what use could be made, in the public interests, of the unplantable land that has been acquired with a group of forest areas in the neighbourhood of Lough Long, Lough Goil, and Loch Eck in Argyllshire.

The Committee proposed that the whole area should be used as a National Park under the Commission and made convenient for ramblers and campers. An agreement was arrived at with the Glasgow Corporation, which owns some of the land as a water Catchment area; and the Commission is now in charge. It has marked out paths, set apart camping places and provided a number of hostels in co-operation with different Associations.

The experience of the working of this first National Park is so favourable that a repetition of the scheme in other places is now being arranged for. We may therefore anticipate that, before long, the Forestry Commission will have gathered experience in these matters and will be able to act for the National Authority in many places, when the time happily arrives that such an Authority has been brought into being.

There is no doubt about the keenness of multitudes of people, especially of young people, to spend their week-ends or holidays in some of the charming districts that would be reserved. If only we could obtain an Authority that would encourage access to these places in a sensible way, and emancipate us from so many notices that "Trespassers will be Prosecuted" on places where trespassers cannot possibly do any harm, many people would become aware for the first time of some of the beauties of their native land, and all sorts of health-giving Associations would spring up around them.

There is no need to fear the crowd. There is plenty of room on our heaths and hills and downlands for all those who are prepared to walk. The pity is that the enjoyment of them has been denied so long.

Chapter XX

Conclusion

The Need for a Ministry of Agriculture and Food Supplies—Its Relation to the National Agricultural Commission—Concluding Summary of Impressions.

THERE ARE TWO important administrative questions that should be referred to before I try, in conclusion, to summarise the case we have been considering. They are the status of the Ministry of Agriculture and its relation to the National Agricultural Commission.

I have not been behind the scenes since 1931 and can therefore only imagine the Departmental struggles that must have been going on as one who has had an intimate experience of the machinery of government.

You cannot have a coherent and progressive Agricultural Policy that is separated from a Food Policy. They relate to the same subject. Up to the present it has been nobody's business to see that the people are properly fed. It has been left to thousands of different individuals or agencies to develop their enterprises in their own way, with the object, quite naturally, of making as much profit as they can out of them; but it was not their purpose, or within their power, to see that the people were adequately fed.

So far as the Importation of Food has been anybody's business, in the Governmental sense, it has been that of the Board of Trade. But the Board of Trade is not concerned with the objects for which food is imported; it is only concerned with Food Imports in relation with our exports. The fact that the balance of trade is on the adverse side, and that the experience of those who have lent money to foreign nations has been very dismal lately, should induce the Board of Trade to turn a friendly eye on proposals for growing more food at home, but, apart from considerations of this character, they are not concerned.

Since the Ottawa Agreement of 1932 we have witnessed a series of patched-up compromises—bits of Quantitative Regulation, bits of Tariffs and doses of Subsidies, all mixed up and continually changing, which tell as eloquently and plainly as can be of the perpetual struggle that must have been going on between the Ministry of Agriculture and the Board of Trade.

We ought to have a Policy which, as I have often said, aims at supplying the people with abundant food on fair terms and, at the same time, enables the home-producer to contribute his share to that abundance on terms that will give him a secure and happy life and lead to the full and suitable use of our land. We can never hope to develop a Policy that will promote these ends unless it is made the business of a single State Department with a Minister responsible to Parliament and to the Nation for its successful execution.

I well remember the long inter-departmental wrangles that preceded the establishment of a single Ministry responsible for all Health Services, but the commonsense of the proposal is no less obvious in this case than in that. The difficulties in this case are nothing like so great or so deeply rooted in tradition and past practice as were those experienced in creating the Ministry of Health.

We should therefore have a single Ministry of Agriculture and Food Supplies, and unified direction of the whole great business.

The reasons for a National Agricultural Commission, in standing charge of the development of the plans that have been proposed and responsible for their proper execution, is that, from the nature of the case, long-term operations are involved and continuity of experience and direction necessary. The Minister of Agriculture and Food Supplies should be the President of this Commission and finally responsible for its activities. We have to find a compromise between the semi-independence of such a Body as, say, the Electricity Commission and an arrangement that recognises the continued responsibility of the Government for matters that affect the life of the people every day alongside the continued discharge of duties by the Agricultural Commission involving far-reaching plans that require a long time for their execution.

In some respects the Board of the Admiralty is on lines similar to those I am recommending, except that the National Agricultural Commission would not be subject to outside service changes but should have a carefully chosen and efficient personnel with a reasonably long term of office.

Throughout the book I have sought to concentrate attention upon the most important of the changes that ought to be made and have therefore omitted reference to many minor, but valuable, services that attach to land policy. The provision of cottage-holdings and of convenient services for allotment holders are some of these, but a final word must be said on the vital question of the adequate provision of new cottages.

In Chapter V reasons were given for estimating that at least 250,000 cottages are required for agricultural workers. Whatever the number may be, it is certain that we shall never attract back to the land the increased number of workers the plans proposed will require, nor even retain in our villages all the young people who are there already and who would gladly remain if they could be sure of a good home to settle down in, unless the provision of good cottages is continuously pressed forward.

We do not want to duplicate authorities, or divorce the building of new cottages from proper planning or from other developments of village life. For these reasons the present powers and duties of the County Councils should be extended so as to enable them to supply the housing needs as they are formulated in the programmes of the National Commission and its County Committees.

.   .   .   .   .

In conclusion, let me summarise some of the chief considerations that emerge from our examination of the great matter that has been the subject of this book.

We are presented in Great Britain with the continuous decline of a great and vital industry. Those who are responsible for its conduct have been exposed to a recurrence of misfortunes, which are preventible, but inseparable from the present system. These misfortunes have exercised a most depressing influence upon the standard of equipment and conduct of the industry, with the result that, notwithstanding exceptional advantages, a considerable amount of land has gone out of cultivation altogether and millions of acres of good land are insufficiently used.

At the same time many villages and county towns that were once prosperous have become impoverished and present unmistakable evidences of decay. Good agricultural workers, with priceless gifts of craftsmanship and aptitude, have been leaving the countryside for forty years or more until the numbers of those that are left is sometimes insufficient even for the present standards of cultivation. Side by side with all this, and apart from the grave national weakness that it involves, it is now known that multitudes of people are insufficiently supplied with the very foods that our land is specially suited to produce.

I have endeavoured to examine the causes of these things with fairness and without political partisanship. Indeed I can truly say that all my early training and inherited traditions were in the way of trying to find reasons for fortifying the present system. But we cannot escape the inexorable logic of fact.

We ought to have a prosperous countryside. The agricultural industry should be full of enterprise; it should attract ability and make a ready use of the increased powers that advancing knowledge provides us with; above all, it should provide a secure and contented life for those who work in it. Only so far as we can bring these things about can we re-people our villages or make the best of our land.

The causes for the decline that have taken place have not been difficult to discern—indeed some of them are obvious. My most difficult task—as is usually the case—has been to suggest the remedies that are necessary and that can be applied.

I believe the case for the National ownership of Agricultural land is unanswerable. I believe also that the methods that have been propounded for its acquisition are fair in themselves and can be applied without difficulty. The restoration of farm equipment and the other procedures necessary for affording the competent cultivator a proper opportunity are not more than those which a good landlord should be willing to provide. The State must be a good landlord.

The procedures recommended for providing that reliability of fair price—so essential for the successful conduct of the industry under any system of society—are undoubtedly complicated, but they are infinitely less so than the unseen medley of agencies that levy their toll to day upon producer and consumer alike, and which it is sought to replace by an orderly and reasonable arrangement. The system of paying the producer as low a price as possible and charging the consumer as much as possible is essentially immoral, and must be done away with.

It is necessary also that, coincidently with these procedures, we should have such control over Importation as will secure that abundance of food is provided for the people and that the processes of distribution are not wasteful or unjust.

There is nothing impossible in any of these things. They require only that the National will shall be expressed for their achievement. There is abundance of ability in our midst to manage them successfully.

Once these essentials of well-equipped land and an ordered system were obtained we could go forward to that great expansion of cultivation and food production which has formed the theme of the Third Part of this book. The plans put forward are in accord with the suggestions that have been made by many eminent men of capacity and great knowledge. Experience may lead to their modification in this direction, or in that; but it may be predicted with certainty that growing knowledge, assisted by the unsurpassed advantages of our soil and climate, together with the skill we possess in the arts of husbandry, will lead to their enlargement rather than to their reduction.

There is no enterprise, I believe, more worthy of National effort, more creative of the best wealth, or more pregnant with happiness for the people than the restoration of our neglected countryside.

It is our Land. We love it; every one of us. Let us throw down the challenge to adversity.

APPENDIX I

From the Census Returns. 1.

The Numbers of Male Persons Returned as Occupied in Agriculture and Horticulture in Great Birtain in the Years 1891, 1911, 1921, 1931 and 1936.

ENGLAND AND WALES

Year	Employers (a)	Workers (b)	Total
1891	313,398	904,859	1,218,257
1911	364,602	747,209	1,111,811
1921	385,344	743,313	1,128,657
1931	365,283	698,420	1,063,703
1936	(e)	636,000 (d)	(e)

SCOTLAND

Year	Employers (c)	Workers (b)	Total
1891	69,969	109,477	179,466
1911	70,683	88,259	158,942
1921	60,938	98,050	158,988
1931	63,326	90,688	154,014
1936	(e)	91,000	(e)

GREAT BRITAIN

Year	Employers	Workers	Total
1891	383,367	1,014,336	1,397,701
1911	435,285	835,468	1,270,753
1921	446,282	841,363	1,287,645
1931	42 609	789,108	1,217,717
1936	(e)	727,000 (d)	(e)

1. These figures from the Census Returns will be found to exceed those given in Part 1 of the Annual Agricultural Statistics which refer only to those employed on Holdings above one acre in extent.

(a) Includes farmers, graziers, relatives assisting in the work of the farm, farm bailiffs, foremen and those engaged in Horticultural Occupations included under the headings "Managerial" and "Working on Own Account".

(b) Includes agricultural labourers and farm servants and those engaged in Horticultural Occupations included under the headings "Operatives", "Out of Work" "and Others or no Statement".

(c) Includes farmers, graziers, crofters, relatives assisting farmers and crofters, grieves and foremen and those engaged on horticultural occupations included under the headings "Managerial" and "Working on Own Account".

(d) Based on the percentage change in agricultural workers between 1931 and 1936.

(e) Figures not available.

APPENDIX II

Land Statistics

GREAT BRITAIN

	Arable Land		Permanent Grass		Total Acreage under Crops and Grass
Year	Acres	Year	Acres	Year	Acres
1891	16,484,664	1891	16,433,850	1891	32,918,514
1911	14,647,788	1911	17,446,870	1911	32,094,658
1921	14,967,303	1921	15,906,372	1921	30,873,675
1931	12,634,358	1931	17,281,162	1931	29,915,520
1936	12,095,761	1936	17,359,730	1936	29,455,491

GREAT BRITAIN

Rough Grazings[1]	
Year	Acres
1891	([2])
1911	12,875,660
1921	14,312,139
1931	14,813,294
1936	15,844,177

[1] Includes land in Deer Forests used or capable of being used for grazing.

[2] Information not available.

APPENDIX III

Compensation on Nationalisation of Land

Contributed by Ernest Davies

THE TASK HERE undertaken is to suggest a fair way in which agricultural land can, with least disturbance, be simply and cheaply transferred to the State. Cash purchase is ruled out as it would involve the raising of large loans on the market which might be costly and difficult and might reduce Government borrowing ability required for other purposes. The method suggested is purchase in securities of a Land Corporation which should be formed and in which land would be vested. This land corporation would be financially self-dependent. It would administer a Land Fund which should be at least self balancing, the object being for all outgoings to be covered by revenue. All rents on publicly owned land would be payable to the fund, while financial outgoings would include interest on land securities and contributions to sinking funds for redemption of stocks.

Securities of the Land Corporation would consist both of those created to buy out existing owners, i.e. stock given as purchase price, and those issued for development purposes either through public issue or raised from Government sources for the Land Fund. Security would therefore be income from nationalised land and the assets of the Land Corporation, namely the land itself.

The lower the rate of interest payable and the greater the Fund's income, the quicker could these stocks be reduced. The lower the rate of interest the greater the financial benefit the farmer could receive from land nationalisation, in the form of lower rents, and the quicker total redemption is effected the sooner will interest charges disappear and the full advantages from nationalisation be realised. Through redemption of Land stock, therefore, interest burden would gradually be reduced and land become the unencumbered property of the nation.

The lowest possible interest rate being that at which the Government can borrow, a Government guarantee of interest and principal would help the maximum benefits to be achieved in the miminum of time.

It is not necessarily wise for Government as a matter of course to guarantee all stocks of all public corporations created to run nationalised industries. The giving of excessive guarantees might worsen Government credit and increase the cost of Government borrowing, which in any case would be heavy in the early days of a Labour Government. Further, the cost of compensation when industries were acquired would be raised if the rate of interest was increased in this way.

There is, nevertheless, a strong argument in favour of guaranteeing land stocks. In the case of different industries it is not impossible to assess the values of the industries to be acquired and the probable income based on past experience and estimated future production. In the case of land the problem is more difficult owing to the multitude of owners, different circumstances in which land is owned and for which it is used. A further consideration is the all important role that prosperity on the farm plays in the life of the community and the necessity for the immediate and visible success of land nationalisation when effected by a Labour Government. The quicker land is freed from interest charges the greater the benefit in the form of lower rents, etc.

As Government guaranteed stock is among the highest forms of securities, income on it would be far more secure than rent from agricultural land or mortgage interest. This would assure greater market value and marketability of Land stock than of land itself at the present time, and would justify more favourable capitalisation. That is to say from Government guaranteed Land stock a lower income should be received than was received from the land for which it was exchanged. Looked at from another angle it would be considered that previous income from the land was justifiably higher because its receipt was less certain.

If no other considerations were to be taken into account, the nominal value of land producing a high income could be replaced by Land stock of the same nominal value, which should produce a lower income. By way of example only, suppose land valued at £10,000 produced a net rent of £500 per annum. If it were replaced by £10,000 of Land stock on which a Government guaranteed rate of interest of $3\frac{1}{2}$ per cent per annum was paid, the income would be only £350. If other factors entered in and, for purposes of compensation, the valuation of the land was reduced to, say, £9,000, the new income would be only £315 compared with the previous income of £500.

Land would be purchased in Land Corporation stock. The actual rate of interest payable on it might be fixed in the Act nationalising the land or left to the Minister to decide in consultation with the Treasury. The rate should be fixed, however, before any valuation took place to determine the amount of stock to be given. The margin between that received in the past and that receivable in the future would be to the Land Corporation's advantage and leave sums available for paying off the stock. How much of this margin would be used for redemption would of course depend on policy. For instance, if it is desired to use the Land Fund for development rather than raise additional money for that purpose, it would be necessary to sacrifice quick redemption and draw on the margin. If, on the other hand, it were felt that money could easily and cheaply be raised for development, and if it were desired to pay off the stock given as compensation as speedily as possible, then quick redemption would be called for. No doubt, however, there would be other charges on the margin such as reduction of excessive rents or other adjustments.

The greater the surplus of receipts over the amount of interest payable, the quicker could stock given as compensation be paid off and the annual interest charge reduced and finally abolished. Because Government guaranteed Land stock would rightly produce a lower income than similarly valued land, the income of the Land Fund would be greater than interest charges on Land Corporation stock and leave a margin large enough to redeem it over a comparatively short period.

To the owner of the stock, that is in the first instance the compensated landlord, the most important consideration is the continuance of income. The greater the certainty of income and the better the security, the lower the income he will be willing to accept. If that security is readily marketable and he desires a greater income he can always realise the compensation and make use of the money at greater risk for higher income. The Land stock could be sold and the proceeds invested elsewhere. As the Land Corporation will be required by statute to redeem its stock within a specified period by purchase below 100 or drawings at 100, there is always likely to be a market resulting from purchasing for the sinking fund if the price falls below 100.

It is suggested that the Act should provide that the amount of compensation should be a number of years purchase of the income tax assessment under Schedule A. Schedule A is based on an assessment of what a landlord should be able to get from his property annually. If he himself occupies the premises and lives rent free it is the income which he would derive were he to let the premises. For this purpose a valuation is made every five years known as the Quinquennial Valuation to determine "the gross annual value of the property". By "gross annual value" is meant the rent which it is considered could be obtained if the property were let in the open market assuming that the owner would pay the necessary repairs and the tenant the rates. As this assessment is made every five years and as the landlord can always appeal against it, it is logical to assume that the assessment is reasonable and that it could serve as a starting-off point for valuation purposes.

The problem will be how many years' purchase to apply. To fix now for a problematical time ahead any definite number would be as difficult as it would be unwise. The actual number must depend largely upon conditions prevailing at the time, because conditions today may be very different from what they will be when Labour introduces an Act to nationalise agricultural land. Further, complete nationalisation is likely to be a process extending over a period of years, agricultural land in one district being nationalised first and in others later. Conditions also may vary from district to district. It may well be that the ultimate decision may be something between fifteen or twenty years' purchase of Schedule A Assessment. At the present time the latter looks on the high side and the former on the low. This final determination could be made by a national tribunal of three to be appointed by Treasury minute immediately it has been decided to introduce the nationalising Bill. This procedure has great advantages. It enables much time to be saved as the Tribunal can deliberate while the Bill is going through its various stages and it might well publish its decision in time for it to be incorporated in the Bill in its final stage. It further permits specific instructions to be given in the minute creating the Tribunal and these would include directions as to how the decision should be arrived at and what should be taken into account and what ignored. This procedure was followed with marked success in determining the amount of compensation to be given to coal royalty owners.

The Tribunal's decision would be the basis of compensation once the Act was passed. Then as it was decided to nationalise land in different districts, notice would be served by the Land Corporation on all owners of land that it proposed to take over their land and issue to them in payment Land stock to the extent of a valuation made on this basis. Negotiations would then proceed between the

Land Corporation and the owner and any minor adjustments necessary could be made and the amount agreed upon. All expenses of transfer would be paid by the Land Corporation.

If the Landowner were of the opinion that such compensation was unreasonable and could show good cause for appeal, he could do so. Grounds on which an appeal could be made would have to be specified in the Act and the more difficult appeal was the better, as long as justice was done.

In any area where acquisition by the State was to take place, District Valuation Tribunals would have to be appointed. These tribunals should be composed of those best versed in knowledge and experience of local land values, e.g., Local Government valuation officials, representatives of Commissioners of Inland Revenue and the Land Valuation Department, etc. Appeal would therefore be made to a District Tribunal which would hear the case of the owner. From this there would be no appeal except on a matter of law. Where an appeal was granted, the Tribunal would proceed to assess the value of the land on an alternative basis, that of the 1919 Acquisition of Land Act. It would fix a value on the basis of a price which a willing seller might be expected to receive from a willing buyer at a hypothetical sale in the open market. In doing this it would have to follow certain instructions which would be laid down in the principal Act. These would include the following:—

1. No allowance should be made on account of acquisition being compulsory, nor of any increased value which might result from the land's transfer to the State.
2. The land should be valued as used for agricultural purposes only, i.e. no allowance for existing or possible future site value.
3. Regard should be had to the relation of the land owner to fixed capital equipment and its value and condition, where the landowner was responsible.

4. Account should be taken of any likely decline in the value of the land as the result of probable statutory control were State acquisition not taking place, e.g. restrictions on use.

5. Consideration should be given to any return and assessment of capital value for taxation where relevant.

6. No allowance should be made for undeveloped mineral rights.

To sum up. If the owner were satisfied that the original valuation was fair or negotiations adjusted any small differences, he would accept the amount and the matter would be closed with the issue to him of the Land stock on the transfer of the land to the State. If, on the other hand, he were not satisfied that this valuation was justified and had grounds for appeal, he would do so knowing that an alternative valuation on the principle of the 1919 acquisition of Land Act would be made by the impartial District Tribunal. In other words, the Act would require in the first place the application of the number of years purchase to Schedule A assessment as determined by the National Tribunal. The landowner would have the right to appeal from this where it was reasonable to do so in favour of a valuation on the basis of the Acquisition of Land Act. In this way the landowner would be protected from too arbitrary a valuation and local differences could be allowed for.

Different Classes of Landowners

The above applies in general to nationalisation of agricultural land, but in dealing with different classes other considerations arise and can be dealt with in detail as follows:—

(1) Landlords

Landlords are here considered as those whose relationship to the land is purely that of the recipient of rent. In their case another consideration enters in as net income is known and this might need to be taken into account. It certainly should where excessive rents are being charged or where the landlord failed to carry out his responsibilities. To the extent that Schedule A reflected these excessive rents, valuation on the normal basis would generally over-compensate the landlord. It is necessary, therefore, to provide machinery to take into account varying rents and the good and bad landlord.

To enable this to be done if the Land Corporation can make out a case for valuation on the alternative basis of the Acquisition of Land Act valuation, one should be made by the Tribunal. The Act could name conditions that would warrant this alternative basis, such as the charging of rents in excess of those normally prevailing for similar land, the failure of the landlord to live up to his responsibilities, or other special considerations, many of which might arise from the old leases. If the Tribunal were satisfied that a case existed for this valuation in accordance with the Act, it shall proceed to make it on the basis of the Land Acquisition Act. In determining the price that a willing seller could be expected to obtain, account would have to be taken of instructions already referred to and in addition the reasonableness of the rents charged and the probability of their continuance, the nature of the fixed charges deducted and their likelihood of change, the condition of the land and the extent to which the landlord had fulfilled his responsibilities. This last would include the provision of and state of buildings, fixed equipment, etc., for the supply and structural upkeep of which the landlord was responsible or where he had a reversionary interest in them.

The general principle suggested earlier of allowing the landowner to appeal against the amount determined by applying the Schedule A basis would still apply where the Land Corporation had not made out a case for this alternative valuation. If such an appeal were made, similar factors would be taken into account by the Tribunal as in the case when the Land Corporation itself had sought the alternative valuation.

(2) *The Owner-Occupier*

Here the determination of values presents greater difficulty. The owner-occupier pays no rent and when his land is acquired by the State he would normally be charged rent by the State. Offsetting this there would of course be the interest on the Land stock he received as compensation, but it needs no great imagination to envisage the cry that would go up from the farmer who owns his farm if he were suddenly called upon to pay rent. The confusion and misunderstanding that would arise in his mind over the receipt of interest on stock with which he was presented on the one hand and the demand for rent on the other, would probably cause resentment and ill-feeling. If he did not quite understand what was happening he would feel he was being "done". There is a way out of this difficulty, which is suggested under "Basis C" below. First, however, it is necessary to examine the basis of compensation already suggested as it would apply if no special treatment were meted out to the owner-occupier.

On the face of it the application of so many years pur-chase to the assessment value under Schedule A of the income tax can be easily applied in the case of the owner-occupier. But in accepting this, two new vital considerations enter in. First the condition of the land and second the income derived from it. The owner-occupier has himself been responsible for the upkeep of the land and its value must in part at least depend upon the use to which the land has been put and the care with which its fertility has been preserved, etc. This will be reflected in the income derived from the land which is in part governed by its productivity, e.g. comparable yield per acre of crops produced. Possibly, therefore, Schedule A assessment and the compensation resulting from this basis should be adjusted upwards or downwards according to a report on the condition of the land and the results from farming it, after inspection and investigation by representatives of the proposed National Agricultural Commission.

Perhaps a scheme could be devised whereby quality of farming could be graded with a specified basis as the norm and any improvement or deterioration of this being allowed for in fixing compensation. To take Schedule A values purely and simply might result in over compensation, as the net annual value of land occupied by the owner is purely hypothetical. If the value is too great, over-compensation would result, and if too low the farmer would either pay too low a rent to the State or if he paid the correct rent, he would be penalised by receiving an insufficient income from his stock to cover it. To reward the good farmer and penalise the bad in fixing compensation is equitable.

A fairer way of arriving at a base for compensation from which necessary adjustments could be made, might be the owner-occupier's actual income-tax assessment. The owner-occupier is not only taxed on the above Schedule A basis as a landlord but additionally as he engages in farming for profit. For this purpose he can choose between Schedule B which is gross annual value as taken for Schedule A excluding the value of his farmhouse, or taxation on actual results under Schedule D. This last is the equivalent in treating farming as a trade engaged for in profit the net income being taxed. If the farmer chooses wisely he takes the schedule under which he pays the least income-tax. If he chooses Schedule D it would mean his profits were less than the gross annual value which was suggested as one basis for compensation. This Schedule D might serve as a basis if the amount of compensation were to be determined according to the use to which land had been put and its profitability. It would be the nearest possible equivalent to the Labour Party's basis of net maintainable reasonable revenue. Returns over a period—say three years at least —would have to be examined, as where a farmer elects to be taxed according to his profits he can set off losses over a

limited period against them. Average profits would therefore have to be taken. A second basis for compensation
purposes could therefore be the number of years purchase
as fixed by the National Tribunal applied to actual
income-tax assessment. There is probably little advantage
of this over Schedule A and it is put forward merely as an
alternative without enthusiasm.

Basis C

The owner-occupier is the most important of all farmers;
he occupies at least one-third of the farmland of the
country and is the one to be most encouraged. It is highly
desirable to keep him on the land, and every inducement
should be made to keep him there. If he is given special
consideration on the nationalisation of land, such an
inducement will exist. With this in view this method of
compensation is proposed. To compensate the owner-
occupier by giving him marketable Land stock might
tempt him to turn his compensation into cash when he
strikes a bad period and leaves the land. If this happened
it would be a fatal result of nationalisation. To compensate
on any of the above bases would be in the main simply to
hand the owner actual Land stock on which he received
interest, which interest he would then hand back to the
Land Corporation as rent for the use of the land. To
eliminate this and to disturb him the least and to prevent
misunderstanding on the part of the farmer as to what was
really happening, which would be bound to arise, the
owner could be left in possession of his land *rent free*. The
land would be subject to an inspection by the National
Agricultural Commission to satisfy it that it was well
farmed and in good condition. A further possible condition
would be that the owner was agreeable to carry out experiments and to farm it within any general plan devised,
including willingness to amalgamate with other farms. He
could remain in possession of his land as long as he continued to farm the land. On his death this could apply to
his family for, say, twenty years. If he desired to dispose of

the land in whole or in part he could only do so with the Land Corporation's permission if he were able to find another farmer-occupier or if the State were willing to take possession itself. In such cases he would then receive compensation on the bases of the assessed value at the time of nationalisation less any necessary adjustments for depreciation, deterioration or bad use of soil, etc. While in the first place no issue of stock to the owner-occupier would have taken place, the land would have automatically been vested in the Land Corporation and a valuation on the number of years' purchase of Schedule A at the time of original nationalisation would be made. As such valuations could be delayed it would relieve the Tribunals of valuing all land to be nationalised at the same time.

As rents charged in other cases would cover not only interest but sinking-fund charges to enable stock to be redeemed as speedily as possible, as suggested at the outset, the owner-occupier would enjoy a double advantage. He would live rent free and would make no contribution to the redemption of stock given as compensation. The Land Fund would not suffer materially as no stock would be issued until the occupier or his heirs up to the limited period ceased to farm the land. All it would mean would be that while there was no rent coming into the fund from land farmed by ordinary owner-occupiers there would be no outgoings in interest charges. The Fund would only suffer to the extent that the rent it could have charged on the land exceeded the interest it would have had to pay out. As the owner-occupier would naturally object if he were asked to pay rent in excess of the interest he received on the Land stock given as compensation, this surplus would, in effect, be non-existent.

Should, while still in possession, the owner-occupier require working capital it would be an easy matter for the Land Corporation to have an arrangement with the Agricultural Mortgage Corporation whereby the latter had a lien on the equivalent amount of Land stock that would be issued as compensation in the future. This would be a great help as many farmers lack the funds to keep their capital equipment in repair or up to date.

Mortgages

A great quantity of land is mortgaged in the case of both the landlord and the owner-occupier. In some cases the high interest rates charged are a burden on the farmer and handicap him in making the best use of his farm. The mortgagee can be dealt with by having his mortgage paid off in Land stock taken from that given as compensation. As for the most part the security of Land stock must be greater than the credit of the mortgagor, the lower rate of interest is likely to be acceptable to the owner of the mortgage. Should it be necessary for him to obtain a higher income or should the life of the stock be longer than that of the mortgage and he need cash, he could always sell the Land stock.

The amount of Land stock to be given the mortgagee could be agreed upon between him and the landlord, but if agreement could not be reached the District Tribunal could act as arbitrator. In the case of the owner-occupier the Tribunal in assessing compensation could determine the amount to be given in place of the mortgage. In both cases the Tribunal in assessing the amount of Land stock to be given to the mortgagee would consider the security of the mortgage, i.e. the extent to which the land was mortgaged up to its value, the credit of the mortgagor, previous regular payment of interest, etc. As in no case would the Tribunal award greater compensation than the value of the land, the mortgagee would clearly lose if his mortgage were greater than that value. Possibly he should have the right to appeal to the Tribunal for special treatment where the decline in value was due to no fault of his own, but he should not be compensated to the extent that he had advanced too much any more than an investor who buys securities at too high a price would be compensated.

In the case of the owner-occupier, if this procedure were followed, the mortgagee would obtain Land stock from

the Land Corporation and the owner-occupier would have
to pay the equivalent of the interest and redemption charge
on it to the Land Corporation in lieu of mortgage interest.
To eliminate this complication it would be preferable to
transfer the mortgage to the Agricultural Mortgage
Corporation (who would charge their rate of interest).
This non-profit-making corporation, set up in 1928,
would presumably become more of a Government concern
under a Labour Government. As security for the mortgage
this corporation would have a lien on the Land stock
ultimately to be issued as compensation similarly to the
manner suggested for new mortgages above. The mortgagee
could then receive stock of the mortgage corporation
instead of Land stock which would be preferable. In the
above ways the private usurer as far as the farmer is
concerned would be got rid of and the crippling effect
of heavy interest rates eased. This would result because,
in effect, the farmer would have his mortgage interest
reduced to the rate of interest paid on Land Corporation
stock or to the rate charged by the Agricultural Mortgage
Corporation. If the Land stock carried a Government
guarantee, as suggested, the rate of interest paid by the
farmer would almost certainly normally be less than
that which he is now paying, or which he would be asked
to pay by private lenders.

APPENDIX IV

Land Owned by Public Bodies

	Area (Acres)	Remarks
Ministry of Agriculture and Fisheries	10,127	Acquired under the Small-Holdings Colonies Acts and the Sailors and Soldiers (Gifts for Land Settlement) Act and still retained on the 31st March 1937. Including 1,193 acres of leased land.

	Area (Acres)	Remarks
Forestry Commission .	957,000	
Admiralty . . .	7,690	
Air Ministry . . .	41,000	
Crown Lands . . .	220,000	
Royal Parks (Office of Works)	5,620	
Home Office . . .	2,465	As at November 1936.
War Office . . .	207,906	
Commission for Special Areas . . .	691	
Department of Agriculture for Scotland (including land acquired for small-holdings) . . .	432,850	

Duchy of Cornwall . .	126,056	
Duchy of Lancaster . .	18,000	
Ecclesiastical Commissioners . . .	239,000	These figures relate to 1927.
Oxford University . .	175,856	
Cambridge University .	115,528	

	Area *(Acres)*	*Remarks*
Local Authorities: England and Wales — County Councils and County Borough Councils, for purposes of small-holdings as at 31st December 1936		
(a) owned . . .	406,126	
(b) leased . . .	58,165	
Local Authorities for purposes of allotments as at 31st December 1934 .		
(a) Owned . . .	21,496	
(b) Leased . . .	30,370	
(c) Land entered under Section 10 of the Act of 1922	211	
(d) Land held for other public purposes . .	7,167	
County Councils: For purposes of agricultural education . . .	6,500	As at November 1936 (excluding certain small demonstration plots, sites of houses, etc., which in the aggregate would not total more than 100 acres).
	————	
	3,089,823	

APPENDIX V

Values of Principal Foods 1935-36

	Home-Produced £		Imported[1] £
Wheat . .	9,887,500 @ 6s. 3d. per cwt.		33,684,000
Barley . .	5,856,000 @ 8s. ,,		4,180,000
Oats . .	11,059,500 @ 6s. 1d. ,,		1,038,000
Beef and Veal	35,860,000	. . .	21,846,982
Mutton and Lamb .	21,100,000		17,344,980
Pig Meat .	24,240,000	. . .	34,216,145
Potatoes .	16,990,000	. . .	3,330,196
Eggs . .	18,770,000	. . .	10,625,712[2]
Poultry(dead)	4,876,475	. . .	1,687,000
Milk . .	48,700,000	. . .	—
Butter . .	4,937,400	. . .	44,026,720
Cheese . .	2,931,000	. . .	7,156,827
Other Milk Products .	3,740,700	. . .	— 1,155,187
Fruit . .	8,630,007[3]	. . .	7,450,284
Vegetable and Glasshouse	25,015,000	. . .	5,420,000[4]
Paid for Sugar Beet E. and W. . .	5,690,000	. . . .	— [5]
Feeding-stuffs for Animals	Not ascertained	. .	7,709,000
	248,073,575		200,871,033

[1] Products not akin to home productions are omitted.

[2] Includes Liquid and Dried eggs to the value of £1,773,452.

[3] Apples, Pears, Cherries, Plums, Strawberries, Raspberries, Black, White and Red Currants and Gooseberries. The estimate of £300,000 is included in this figure as approximately that of Scottish produce.

[4] The importation figures relate to Onions and Tomatoes only.

[5] The equivalent value of imported raw sugar is not a comparable figure. Home production of sugar is approximately 28·7 per cent of our total consumption.